CW00866020

Adventures From Middlesex

Edited By Megan Roberts

First published in Great Britain in 2019 by:

Young Writers
Remus House
Coltsfoot Drive
Peterborough
PE2 9BF
Telephone: 01733 890066
Website: www.youngwriters.co.uk

Foreword

Dear Reader,

You will never guess what I did today! Shall I tell you? Some primary school pupils wrote some diary entries and I got to read them, and they were EXCELLENT!

They wrote them in school and sent them to us here at Young Writers. We'd given their teachers some bright and funky worksheets to fill in, and some fun and fabulous (and free) resources to help spark ideas and get inspiration flowing.

And it clearly worked because WOW!! I can't believe the adventures I've been reading about. Real people, make-believe people, dogs and unicorns, even objects like pencils all feature and these diaries all have one thing in common – they are JAM-PACKED with imagination!

We live and breathe creativity here at Young Writers – it gives us life! We want to pass our love of the written word onto the next generation and what better way to do that than to celebrate their writing by publishing it in a book!

It sets their work free from homework books and notepads and puts it where it deserves to be – OUT IN THE WORLD! Each awesome author in this book should be **super proud** of themselves, and now they've got proof of their imagination, their ideas and their creativity in black and white, to look back on in years to come!

Now that I've read all these diaries, I've somehow got to pick some winners! Oh my gosh it's going to be difficult to choose, but I'm going to have SO MUCH FUN doing it!

Bye!

Megan

Contents

Isaac Cook (10)	93
Gabriella Butler (10)	94
Ella Miller (10)	95
Aoife Grimwood (10)	96
Charlie Hobbs (10)	97
Genevieve Hodge	98
Madeline Rose Evans (10)	100
Sam Dylan Mausolle (10)	101
James White (10)	102
Sam Robert Shepherd (10)	104
Jacob Courtney Maycock-Prime (9)	105
Emily Isla Byrne (9)	106
Bethany Anderson	107
Emily Walles (9)	108
Josh Giblett (9)	109
Lewis Hyman (9)	110
Edith Beatrice Butler (10)	111
Luca Stansbury (10)	112
Liam Blakley (9)	113

Preston Park Primary School, Wembley

Rylee Kyan Leach (9)	114
Zeynab Shirzad (8)	116
Mohammed Samir El Kordy (10)	118
Ziad Lloyd (9)	119
Micah Levi Hibbert (9)	120
Namo Wurmezyar (9)	121
Ismaeel Ali (9)	122
Abigail Ayomikun Ogunlami (9)	123
Andrei Ionut Antonie (9)	124
Amira Elmi (7)	125
Iakshmi Sahasra Veluri (9)	126
Anushri Saha (9)	127
Param Bhatt (8)	128
Rayan Salarzai (9)	129
Gabriela Orlinova Sirenyakova (9)	130
Nicole Florentina Pasca (9)	131
Tahar Bnouni (9)	132
Vinithan Kamaleswaran (9)	133
Leart Thaci (9)	134

Diyana Kanbi (8)	135
Laksh Patel (9)	136
Lorena Maya Szabo (9)	137
Precious-Lyla Bridget Turgut (11)	138

Willow Tree Primary School, Northolt

Annabel Bernard (10)	139
Rosa Hosseini (11)	140
Skye Nicholson (10)	142
Jemimah Esi Sackey (10)	144
Alex Wirekoh (10)	146
Ilyas Omar (10)	148
Melissa Andrea Mihaila (11)	150
Jay Hughes (11)	151
Tiffany Elena Nastasiu (11)	152
Ali Shidane (11)	153
Zara Delfi (10)	154
Samuel Xavier Third (10)	155
Noris Ciobotea (10)	156
Anjali Kumar (11)	158
Faizan Arshad (10)	159
Abishna Bavan (10)	160
Kaizer Santillan (10)	161
Saad Arshad (11)	162
Prisha Anand Panchal (10)	163
Wisdom Djan (10)	164
Nelly Alina Siddiqi (10)	165
Ariba Ashiq (10)	166
Mohammed Ayangar (9)	167
Sherry Ayazi (10)	168
Toby Stamford Frost Fountain (11)	169
Nosia Ahmadi (11)	170
Willow Gayle (10)	171
Ryan Kennedy (11)	172
Imran Thomas Ibrahim (9)	173
Anastazja Budzik (9)	174
Willow Welsh (11)	175
Sharon Thomas (10)	176
Callum Ashley Burt (10)	177
Jeshan Jega (9)	178

The Diaries

The Incredible Diary Of... The Trip To Afghanistan

Dear Diary,

Today, I'm going to tell you about my trip to Afghanistan. It was the summer holidays and we thought of going on holiday to Afghanistan, but the problem was that we needed to find good tickets. Finally, we found good tickets from Heathrow Airport to Dubai, then Afghanistan.

We went with British Airlines to Dubai, then we went with Emirates to Kabul, Afghanistan, which was a fourteen hour journey in total. Our cousins were already waiting for us there. We got ready at the airport because it was my cousin's party on the same day. I nearly fell asleep on the journey to the party. Then, finally, we got there.

When we got there, the first thing I did was go to the vending machine. With the help of my teacher, I knew how to use the money. We had more parties, but there was nothing special about them. We also went to a place that had a big field and a freezing swimming pool. The place in our language is called Chilten. We had more exciting journeys, but when we were going back, I was crying so much that my vision wasn't good.

Nahal Shah (10)
Byron Court Primary School, Wembley

The Worst Day Of My Life

An extract

Dear Diary,

Today was the most traumatic day I've ever experienced! It was the day I ended up in the hospital in excruciating pain.

It all started on the joyous occasion of Diwali when I went to my cousin's house to watch bursts of rainbow colours enter the dark, auspicious night. Now, looking back, I wish I hadn't been at that place at that time; it was a death-defying experience which hasn't only stained my finger, but my memory as well. Why was I so careless? The best day of the year was ruined.

The rockets that had painted the sky had faded and the sparklers sat in a bunch, burnt, near the doorstep where the dreadful incident happened. I wonder will my finger ever look the same? Work in the same way?

The catherine wheel was all set. I rushed inside to avoid the danger but little did I know it was right in my path. I stood at the door, my hands clutched onto the frame as I unzipped my boots. *Slam!* Without knowing my hand was there, someone had slammed the door on my finger. My eyes blurred as they began to fill with water. A stream was pouring down my cheeks as I felt the adrenaline. It was like blood pumping through my veins. As my finger got rinsed in cold water, a scream escaped me. The blood, pain, the throbbing - which one pained me the most? Scarlet blood made a trail everywhere.

My pinky had been replaced by a red balloon as it was wrapped in a bandage and then I was rushed to the car. My dad weaved in and out through the traffic until I was at the hospital. Although we zoomed to hospital, I had to wait six hours! Can you believe that?

Shiony Halai (10)
Byron Court Primary School, Wembley

The Discovery Of Time Travelling

Dear Diary,

It all started when I wanted to know what will happen in the future and if we will live on Mars, so I went to my mum who is a scientific explorer and asked her if there could be such a thing as time travelling. She said there could be but there could be no such thing too. Then my mum said, "Why don't we look for it? We will check and discover different science labs while looking for the force of time travelling."

I said, "Why not?"

So then we got out of the house and went to every single science lab that we knew. Suddenly we approached this gruesome and neglected science lab and I felt scared. There were thorns and needles around it, and dirt had really dressed up the place. My mum and I decided to go in and once we had got in, I felt this tingle around my index finger. The tingle started turning into electrical shocks and they were very painful. I held my mum's hand. In the blink of an eye we'd travelled twenty-eight years later... I had never seen anything like that before! We met this strange girl called Marsha and to introduce herself, she said, "Hello, welcome to Mars. I'm Marsha, I am a Martian. I like marshmallows and I do martial

4

arts." She was very weird for the rest of the day. I guess we had found our answer - we can live on Mars and there is the possibility of time travel! I had lots of fun and I didn't have to go through the tingling process again and neither did my mum. The Martians had a portal for time travelling so they let us go through it and now everything is back on track in time!

Emily Zourdani (10)
Byron Court Primary School, Wembley

The Incredible Diary Of... My Holiday To Beirut

Dear Diary,

In the summer holiday, I went to Beirut. I went with my mum, my brothers, my younger sister and my grandma, uncle, auntie and my two cousins. I was very excited to go. We travelled in two different cars. It took a very long time to get to the airport. When we arrived, we entered the airport. It was big and a bit crowded. We had to walk for a long time. We walked through the gate and got onto the aeroplane. I sat down on the puffy seat and waited for take-off.

A few minutes later, the aeroplane finally started moving. It went a bit fast. It felt a bit boring, so I took out my colouring book. After, my cousin gave me some treats.

A few minutes later, the aeroplane landed. Me and my family got out and were in the airport. We found out that the next aeroplane was delayed, so we had to stay in Jordan for a day. We stayed in a hotel near the airport.

In the morning, we got changed and ate breakfast. After we'd got ready to go to the airport, we went on a big red bus. When we arrived at the airport, we went onto the aeroplane straight away. It was a short amount of time in the aeroplane and we got off quickly.

When we were in the airport, we bought food so we could eat. When we went to the bus stop, we waited for the bus. When it came, we got on. We arrived and my mum and my auntie ordered two cars for us. We drove to a big house, there was a big living room with a big sofa and a large shelf. In the kitchen, it was big with a white fridge and freezer. There were big rooms upstairs, there was another room too and there was a large pool!

Lara Eve Alshahbander (7)
Byron Court Primary School, Wembley

The Incredible Diary Of... Going Back In Time

Dear Diary,

Yesterday, I had the most exciting day ever!

After a long day at school, I decided to go to Northwick Park and play football with my friends. As I walked down the road holding my ball in my hand, I tripped over and fell, letting the ball out of my grasp. Determined to have a lovely game of football, I got up and ran after the ball, leading me to a dark, spooky alleyway.

As I rapidly walked down the dirty, damp path, I stumbled upon a dusty phone box. This was very peculiar to me because, if I'm not mistaken, we normally use mobile phones now. Curious and surprised, I opened the door of the phone box.

As I stepped in, I fell down, down, down into a deep black hole, thinking there was no end at all. Before I could think of anything else, I landed on the soft, sandy ground. Shaking because of the unpleasant journey, I stood up with difficulty, staring in amazement at what I saw. Golden, sandy pyramids towered above my head, almost touching the clouds. Grand, beautiful palaces fit for kings stood proudly. It then hit me... I had somehow been transported to the time of the ancient Egyptians!

Suddenly, I heard shouting - somebody was running up to me, waving his arms, bellowing and yelling, "The god has come, oh Tutankhamun!" I am definitely not a god! Just then, out of nowhere, another man started running up to me, carrying golden robes in his arms. "Greetings Rah, God of the Sun, welcome to Egypt. I am Tutankhamun, the one and only pharaoh..."

Sakina Hamir (9)
Byron Court Primary School, Wembley

The Incredible Diary Of... The Magical Portal And The Rainbow Worms

Dear Diary,

Today, I have some news to tell you. Now, I'm sitting in my comfy, swinging chair, laughing at what I did to my husband (he's not my husband any more), Mr Twit. You won't believe me when I tell you...

At six o'clock, I woke up and I was so indignant at what Mr Twit did to me: he tore all of my favourite clothes and dresses into tiny pieces and put them on fire! I looked for revenge. I went outside to relax and to clean some of my angriness but then, a magical door appeared. Some strange-looking, rainbow-coloured worms slithered out.

It was time for revenge! It wasn't like last time (putting disgusting worms in Mr Twit's spaghetti), I had another plan... At that moment, all my angriness left my mind and all of my excitement came back. I stepped into the portal, one foot then the other. They were shaking in excitement. Every bit of my body was shaking! I entered the portal. I was so surprised, my eyes nearly popped off my old face! I saw magical, rainbow humans and elves and worms. There were trillions, quadrillions of the strange worms so I thought I could take 300 of them and put them on my husband. That was the plan.

It took me over two and a half hours to get them in the house. But, I didn't want them in the house, I wanted them on Mr Twit, so I did it. He was so angry that he broke up with me, but I don't really care. My revenge was done!

'Mrs' Twit.

Lana Vacarciuc (10)

Byron Court Primary School, Wembley

My Trip To Jamaica

Dear Diary,

My name's Kianah and I'm ten years old. In April 2018, I went to Jamaica with my dad, step-mum and step-brother, Rhys. In Jamaica, it was nice and hot and we saw family there. Then we stayed at a hotel and went swimming. We also went to a place called Scotchies and had really good jerk chicken at a festival. Also, we saw lots of palm trees and water.

While we were there, we played Marco Polo with a friend we made. There were also lots of restaurants and we tried most of them. We also explored most of Jamaica in just two weeks. We also went to a famous landmark called Dunn's River, it's a waterfall and we climbed it, but then we stopped because I was scared.

Also, when we got out of the airport, my dad called a friend to pick us up and, later on, we got patties from Jamaica in a place called Tastees and they were nice and fresh. It was the best holiday ever and I'll never forget it for the rest of my life. Our room was really big and we went shopping quite a lot. We also played a lot of football and we also went to a kids' club.

In the kids' club, we were going to go on a computer and write a presentation about Jamaica, but then Rhys played Mario and I did some art. Then, we got really good lollipops and tidied up. When we were in Jamaica, we went to a water park and went on the slide and went to a restaurant which had rubbish food and not good service.

Kianah McCarthy Scott (10)

Byron Court Primary School, Wembley

The Incredible Diary Of... The Science Museum

Dear Diary,

I had the best day ever, so let me tell you how it started. First, I woke up at seven o'clock and got ready for school. I had to go to the Science Museum. My mum had to come too. My partner was Amir. He is very funny. We were going on a train to the station called South Kensington.

We went on another train and than we reached there. When we arrived, Mr Mead was talking to my mum. Then, all groups split up and went to different activities. We had to meet up at twelve o'clock.

We did all the activities and experiments. We met up at twelve o'clock, then we had lunch. After that we went to the gift shop and bought stuff. I forgot to say who was in my group! Me, Mario, Ahmed, Mustafa, Alessia and Amir. I got rainbow slime, Mustafa got a squishy, Amir got a foam and a pen, Alessia got a Slinky and Ahmed got nothing. Then, my mum said we had to wait for Mr Mead, but Mr Mead was inside the room with everyone else. There was a lady who explained what we were going to do. She said, "We are going to go inside this room and explore and have fun." There was a slide.

When we'd done all the activities, we went to a science place and they told us about electricity. When they'd finished, we left the museum. We went on the train and another train, then we all came back to school and then we went home.

Piya Shah (7)
Byron Court Primary School, Wembley

The Incredible Diary Of... Sophia!

An extract

Dear Diary,

Today, I had a roller coaster of emotions. It started off with eating a mind-blowing buffet in our hotel in Dubai. Everyone was so excited for breakfast as the buffet looked delicious. Today, we were going on a speedboat near the Palm. As we were getting on the boat, the driver insisted that we had to wear a lifejacket.

Everyone at first was having fun for about half an hour then, suddenly, the boat stopped. None of us had any idea what was going on. At first, we thought there was a landmark nearby for the tour guides to show us, but there wasn't. Everyone was really confused. We were in the same place for half an hour.

Eventually, an elderly man asked the driver what was going on. The driver told us that the engine was broken and we were stranded. It was the scariest moment of my life! My palms were sweating and my knees were shaking. Not only were we stuck in the middle of the ocean, but I can't swim!

I wasn't the only one panicking though, I could see children bawling their eyes out and their parents trying to comfort them. That wasn't all. To make things worse, the radio and signal weren't working so we couldn't call anyone!

My stomach felt as if there were 1,000 butterflies in my tummy having a disco. Trust me, it's worse than you think. Some people even fainted in fear...

Sophia Rana (10)
Byron Court Primary School, Wembley

Nica's Amazing Diary

Dear Diary,

Today, it was my birthday party! My actual birthday is on Monday. I waited silently, watching the clock, waiting for it to be three. Finally, it was time for the party. I sat beside the window, waiting impatiently for my friends to arrive. Me, my mum and my dad had put up banners and decorations around the house.

Eventually, my friends arrived and we rushed to the dining room table to decorate some plain bags. We had glitter glue, beads and other things we could stick on the bags.

After we'd finished, we played around and changed the colour of the lights in my room. We also had an epic pillow fight. I was getting hungry and asked for snacks. Reem, my friend, had eaten all the biscuits! I was shocked! Unfortunately, Lindsay and Safia, my other friends, couldn't make it! We played games and messed about. Me and some of my friends were hiding in the bathroom. It was pitch-back. We used light-up balloons to see. When the pizza arrived, we all sat at the table and ate. We chatted about funny things. We all came downstairs and my mum brought the cake from the kitchen. Everyone sang Happy Birthday to me. People started to leave after that. I had a great time. My dad let me open one present as I have to save the rest for my actual birthday. I got putty and a prank kit. I had the best party ever!

Nica Patel (10)
Byron Court Primary School, Wembley

Jack Murphy's Late!

An extract

Dear Diary,

I don't really know where to start... I guess I should start at school. Today was my first day at Highfield Prep School For Boys. It was all about first impressions. Let's just say that things didn't go so well in primary school. I was Jack Murphy, Geek Boy or Nerdy Murphy just because I brought my homework in on time. Everyone else thought it was an opportunity to take the mickey!

Mummy said that writing it on paper was the best thing to do, so she bought me a diary. I specifically told her not to get me one that said 'Diary' on the front, but nevermind. There I was, sitting at the front of the class, my hand shooting up whenever Mr Wilkins asked a question, then my diary fell out of my bag and who should pick it up but Jonny Lake, the school bully!

Jonny and I have known each other since pre-school and he's taken an interest in making me look like an idiot. He's always done a pretty good job of it. "Dorky Dude's got a diary!" he said, laughing when Mr Wilkins turned. I tried to ignore it like Mummy told me, hoping he'd soon get bored.

When class ended, I was the last one out as everybody had shoved me out of the way. It was no surprise when Jonny kicked my desk over as he went out. "Oopsie!" he said, then ran out to change for games class.

Isra Sussums-Sheikh (10)
Byron Court Primary School, Wembley

The Incredible Diary Of...

An extract

Dear Diary,

I woke up this morning really bored and miserable at 7:30. I slowly stomped down the stairs with heavy feet, thinking it was going to be another boring Sunday. My parents were sat at the dining table and announced the surprise to me, I ran upstairs so excitedly, I even tripped myself up! I had gotten dressed in my tracksuit bottoms and my old, ripped shirt from last year.

For breakfast, we had old, stinky sausages from yesterday and, finally, we were ready to leave at 8:45. We were all feeling excited to go to our grandma's house. When we arrived, we found that we were the last ones there. We all set off in our cars to drive to the farm.

When we got there, we found that our car had broken down, but we would find a way to get back home. First, at 9:20, we decided to go and see the pigs. We found it so funny how they snorted. Next, we went to go see the horses and we got to feed them. I even had a small ride on one of them!

The third animals we were going to see were the chickens, but it was a shame they were all asleep. Finally, we went to go and see the sheep, they were so fluffy and cute. Once we had seen all the animals, we took a photo and decided to eat pizza at 12:50. It was delicious, but I was a little scared as there was a spider right next to me on the bench...

Reem Jabbar (10)

Byron Court Primary School, Wembley

The Incredible Diary Of... My Trip To Florence

Dear Diary,

Last year, during the summer holidays, I went to Italy with my mum, dad and my cheeky but cute little sister. To go to Italy, me and my family had to sit on an aeroplane for two hours. When we arrived, I was full of excitement. We hired a car and my dad drove to Palaia, where my grandparents live.

My favourite place in Italy is called Florence. Ice cream was invented in Florence. To travel there, me and my family took the train for forty-five minutes. We brought some cards so we played different card games.

When we arrived, I went to an indoor cafe and had some hot milk. I went to some shops and it was finally lunch-time. "What a relief!" I said to myself because I was starving. For lunch, I ate a pizza. When we finished lunch, me and my mum went to an outdoor shop while my dad went somewhere I didn't know. My sister took so long to choose who she wanted to go with. Finally, she said that she wanted to go with me and my mum. I bought a butterfly keychain and my sister bought a green dragon keychain with yellow wings. My mum bought a bag keychain.

Then, we met up with my dad and me and my sister had an ice cream and we both had two scoops. At the end of the trip, we got on a train and went back home.

Reika Sofia Ceccanti (8)

Byron Court Primary School, Wembley

The Incredible Diary Of... The Boy Named Rafael

An extract

Dear Diary,

Today was the first day of high school and I had the worst start ever! I always imagined I would walk into the classroom smiling, giving high-fives and fist bumps to everyone. There would be some chit-chat and laughter before the teacher arrived and, when she did, we would all settle down in our seats. We would start our very first lesson and enjoy learning. The break would be super fun because we all would get to know one another. I would have so many friends and would be the most popular among them. The perfect first day... But that was my expectation and it didn't go as I'd hoped it would...

It was a disaster! I arrived at my new school late, so I missed registration. I walked into my class, but it was empty. I was just about to sit myself down when a teacher came and said, "What are you doing here? You should be in the hall right now, getting your timetable."

So, I got my bag and the teacher escorted me to the hall, where the Year 7s were to be welcomed. As I walked in, everyone's eyes were on me. How humiliating, right? My class was sitting right at the front, so I just took the seat near the door. But, the rest of the day was better!

Mishel Shaikh (10)
Byron Court Primary School, Wembley

My Sweet Diary

Dear Diary,

On Sunday, I had an excellent day. I woke up with a big yawn on my face, the sun was shining like a diamond and it was coming through the curtains as a soft breeze touched my face. I could smell the breakfast cooking downstairs. I jumped out of bed and went as fast as I could to the kitchen.

I knew it was going to be a very busy Sunday for me, I had two tournaments - one for badminton and one for cricket. I went with my family to play badminton and, to my surprise, I played so well that I entered the final match! My family and my friends were so excited that they were dancing in the courtyard. I was initially nervous for the final match, but I lived with the pressure and came out with flying colours. In short, I won the match!

My dad reminded me quickly about the cricket match. We were just on time. As my match started, I played so well that our cricket team won the match.

In the evening, I was so tired, but I was happy because I'd had a really nice day as I'd achieved a lot and my family was so proud of me.

We had dinner with my favourite dish and I went to bed thinking of my wonderful day.

Priyesh Suryakant Sakpal (10)

Byron Court Primary School, Wembley

The Incredible Diary Of... Sam's Super Adventure

Dear Diary,

I was walking to school when a shadow fell over me. Something hit the ground. I looked down and I saw drool. Something was breathing on me. I looked up at a winged mammal the size of an elephant... A dragon! It glared at me. I ran and ran like never before.

I saw my friend, Tobias. "Tobias!" I shouted. He looked at me and ran over to me. I told him everything. Suddenly, a portal opened. It came into a spot without a frame. The dragon lifted up his wings and started hovering. Me and Tobias stared at the dragon, it was like we were paralysed!

A jet of fire blasted from his mouth. Me and Tobias ran into the portal and dodged the fire. We came out the other side of the portal. The dragon roared on the other side. It started to come through! Me and Tobias hid behind a tree and heard a growling noise. It was a bear with the body of a lion!

We ran to the portal. The dragon came out and tried to grab us. Suddenly, bats with gigantic hands came.

They tried to catch us, but we dodged them and jumped into the portal. We were back on Earth. The portal closed and Tobias and I ran home.

Joven Ghag (10)
Byron Court Primary School, Wembley

The Incredible Diary Of... Lilly Randeria

Dear Diary,

You'll never guess what happened to me today! Early this morning, Father went to the greedy king's castle. When he came back home, he told me that he had lied to the king and said that I could spin straw into gold! If I did this, I could marry the handsome prince, but if I didn't, I would be killed! I felt like crying because no one can spin straw into gold!

Later that evening, Dad took me to the king's palace. It was ginormous! The towering turrets couldn't be seen behind the puffy clouds. As I walked into the palace, I saw the king at the far end of the magnificent room, sitting on his golden throne.

Just then, the king grabbed me and took me to a room full of straw. He told me to spin it into gold by the morning. Then, he left, slamming the door behind him and leaving me all alone. I started to cry and tears were still dropping off my face hours later.

Then, out of nowhere, this strange goblin appeared. He was dressed in a tattered, red cloak. He told me that he would spin the straw into gold, but only if I gave him my first child. What could I do?

Aneesa Randeria (6)
Byron Court Primary School, Wembley

The Incredible Diary Of... The Great Escape Of Frank The Hamster

Dear Diary,

On Tuesday the 26th of March, my hamster, Frank, escaped. My mum woke up at 11pm to check if he was in his cage and guess what? He wasn't! My mum looked everywhere for him, but she couldn't find him, so she went back to sleep.

An hour later, at midnight, she heard a noise under her bed. It was Frank! She was so close to catching him, but he managed to get away. He ran all the way to my room. Frank squeezed through a gap between my wardrobe and the wall. He then dug a hole into the wall and went into my wall.

My mum came into the room and woke me up. My mum grabbed one of his tubes and put treats in it. He couldn't go into the tube, he was stuck! My heart began to race. My mum grabbed a metal stick and started to push him towards the tube. He went into it and we put the tube in the cage. He came out. We jumped up and down, celebrating.

My mum has now locked the door he came out from (the door on top of the cage). He is now safe in his cage. He is only allowed to have free time in my bath where he can't escape!

Sean Gala (10)
Byron Court Primary School, Wembley

The Day At Sona's House

Dear Diary,

One brilliantly sunny morning, I woke up and went downstairs to have my porridge, then set off for school. In the morning, we did English, a bit of maths and independent reading. After, for lunch, I had a butter and jam sandwich, cheese, crisps and strawberries.

In the afternoon, we did science. Then, Sona's mum came to pick us up. There was quite a problem on the way that I don't want to mention. First, we dashed into Sona's room and got dressed in her clothes. She didn't mind. We played doctors. Because I had a mark on me, I was the patient. Then, we heard Sona's sister playing the piano! Sona's mum then called us downstairs to do some baking. We made chocolate chip cookies. They were so delicious! After, we made a den in Sona's sister's room. We pretended that we were having a sleepover. We sang karaoke. Soon, we were running around, having a pillow fight, then we played Marco Polo.

After, we listened to music and sang songs that we liked. Then, at seven, I went home.

Mahi Mistry (7)

Byron Court Primary School, Wembley

The Incredible Diary Of...

Dear Diary,

I had to go and practise for war. I was really scared, but I had to do it for my country and my family. When I was a kid, I thought it would be fun, but I was wrong.

Lots of people killed themselves to not go to war. It was just horrible. I heard people screaming and I saw smoke, I thought it was the end of my life, but it wasn't. I saw the army planes defending us.

I rushed to the base, but there were no guns. Then, I saw my enemy get shot and instead of running away, I took the enemy's gun to defend myself. Planes fell, people were killed and rockets exploded houses.

At the end of the war, my head was bleeding and I remembered that my dad had died. I stood up and looked for help. I saw some people and they took me to the hospital. Everything went black and I saw my dad. He said to me, "Well done for not giving up."

Over the next few days, I became president and I was really happy. I made a rule that, if anyone fought, they would go to jail.

Eldaras Brazinskas (9)

Byron Court Primary School, Wembley

The Incredible Diary Of... Sir Knight Edward David

Dear Diary,

I have just come back from a tournament and here is how I won the hard, long contest!

I just happened to see the arrogant Sir David as I was walking and he challenged me to a contest which decided the best jouster. He led me to a place called Hadrian's Wall where we had to go for the contest. I was full of doubt when I heard there were three rounds as I'd lost the first one already! I hated that I'd lost already.

Then, there was the second round. I won it! I was happy and joyful, but the final round was the round which decided who won and who lost. My eyes darkened in doubt. I spent hours and hours training for the last round and then, I was ready to joust Sir David.

It was a one-on-one joust and I went for the horse's legs as we fought. Eventually, I made the horse trip and I won the contest as best jouster! Anyway I'm going to catch some sleep now as I'm so tired!

Anirudha Mallik (10)

Byron Court Primary School, Wembley

The Incredible Diary Of... Dwight G Hendrix (My Hamster)

Dear Diary,

Today was the... Hold on, I hear a damsel in distress! Sorry guys, you know how it is... Time for Super Hamster to save the day once again!

Hey guys, I'm back and phew! I mean, it's not every day you get a good old reward for catching a notorious criminal and John has missed out on all of it! I mean, I still don't get the point of school.

Anyway, like I was saying, today was the best day ever! I've just come home from a justice spree and jeez, the journalists just kept on piling up at my door.

Unfortunately for them, the 'exclusive lecture and quotes' will have to wait, after all, it's not every day Felicia wants to go out to dinner with me (we're just friends... kind of) and, anyway, I have about five minutes.

Dudes, time flies when you're having fun. Well, it was nice talking, but I've got a 'date' with Felicia to get to so... peace!

Vasegan Pardeepan (11)
Byron Court Primary School, Wembley

The Incredible Diary Of... The Skiing Sensation

Dear Diary,

On Tuesday the 19th of February 2019, I went to Slovakia. Slovakia is in Europe, near Poland and Hungary. When we got there, we went to Tatralandia for some swimming. The next day, I went to Štrbské Pleso with Ava, Benji, Veronica, Auntie Marne and my mummy.

When we arrived, we all met our skiing instructor, except my mummy because she's been skiing since she was a child and so was able to ski without an instructor. The instructor for me and Ava was called Masha. Each day, we got better and, by the time we got to the last day, we were able to go on the highest mountain there!

On the day we were leaving, we went to a hotel called The Grand Hotel and went swimming in the swimming area. We were all feeling sad that we had to leave Slovakia. On the two hour flight home, I played on my iPad with my best friend, Ava. I felt amazed!

Annemarie Loraine-Grews (8)

Byron Court Primary School, Wembley

My Day In The Concorde Simulator

Dear Diary,

I went to the spectacular Concorde simulator. Aye, it was an amazing experience! I ran into the simulator with excitement. I flew over London, the scenery was beautiful, the sky was so clear that I could see my destination! Then, there was a bang. I must have hit the speed of sound because no alarms went off.

I checked how fast I was going: 987 knots. I was almost about to hit 1k knots! Then, I had to land. I put the nose up to slow down. I had to go under 290 knots to put the landing wheels down. 300 knots. Gosh, that was fast! 287 knots. I put the landing wheels down and put the speed brakes on to slow down even more. I got closer and closer to the runway, then... touched down. It was as smooth as silk. My journey had ended, I'd had a fantastic time! I recommend other people who like planes to go on it too!

Tim Mehmet (10)

Byron Court Primary School, Wembley

The Incredible Diary Of... Clark's Pen Licence

Dear Diary,

Today, I got a pen licence. It was in the morning at nine o'clock. Three other people got it as well. They were: Mark, Aalia and Rukuya. I was so happy when I got my pen licence. I was like, *Mum's gonna be so happy!* My friends were happy because I could stop moaning about it.

I first wrote with my pen in literacy. When I first started writing with my pen, it was hard, but then I got used to it. I was writing with it when I went to Kidz Club with my reading homework. It is so nice, the pen. I like its company. The ink is dark blue, it feels so good to write with a pen, that's why I'm using it.

I'll still use it tomorrow. It feels so nice. I wish I'd gotten it earlier, but I'm happy that I've got my pen licence. I'll never forget today!

Clark Elliott (9)
Byron Court Primary School, Wembley

The Incredible Diary Of... Taalia The Tightrope Walker

Dear Diary,

Today was a wild roller coaster for me at the circus in Paris. I performed my new, astonishing trick. Here's how it went.

Darkness, a single spotlight shone down on me and I wore a black and white bejewelled bodysuit that shimmered in the spotlight. Step by step, I carefully climbed the ladder that led to the tightrope.

As I approached the tightrope, nervousness spread through my shaking body. I took a deep breath and made my way across the piece of rope high above the ground. I paused when I reached the middle. I ran to the end of the tightrope as fast as a cheetah and I unexpectedly did a sensational backflip and landed with a gracious curtsy! Suddenly, the crowd broke out into an almighty roar. I have never felt so proud of myself. It was the best moment of my life!

Aisha Hannah Butt (9)
Byron Court Primary School, Wembley

The Incredible Diary Of... My Incredible Holiday!

Dear Diary,

Today, we were expecting the company of our Thai friend, Nana, and I was looking forward to an amazing barbecue cooked by the chef.

Following a cooling dip in the crystal clear pool, we all got ready in time for Nana's arrival. The villa staff had prepared us a beautifully set table and delicious food, including: octopus, squid, tiger prawns, crab, white snapper and an assortment of sides.

As the sun went down, we enjoyed the lovely food, drink and Nana's company well into the evening. I especially loved the chef's amazing dessert - ice cream, chocolate cake and sticky caramel sauce! Us kids went to bed, Nana stayed up for hours. I could hear her laughing and telling crazy stories! It was a great day with our excitable, funny friend!

Ryaana Kava (10)

Byron Court Primary School, Wembley

Diary Of A KK Kid (Zombie Attack)

Dear Diary,

My classmates and I were sitting in class, listening to my teacher talk about maths non-stop and everyone was bored. Jay rose his hand and asked Miss George, "What's that?" while pointing at a portal.

As soon as Jay said that, the portal sucked everyone in, except him. As soon as everyone landed, guns spawned in our hands and zombies started appearing everywhere. We started to attack them. I had a minigun, so it was easy for me to take them down.

Three-quarters of the class were turned into zombies, but Zakir, Abdullah, Eldaras and I all escaped just in time, but there were more zombies! They placed C-4, thinking it would kill us but, as soon as it exploded, we escaped through the portal and the zombies were dead!

Krystian Keto-Edwards (9)

Byron Court Primary School, Wembley

Going To Portugal

Dear Diary,

I went to Portugal for a week!

On the first day, as soon as we arrived, we went to a restaurant. On the second day, we went shopping and after, we went to the beach. On the third day, we had the great idea of buying a boat! We went to the deep water and the big waves tipped the boat over and we fell into the deep water! On the fourth day, we went to Spain. We found a lion jellyfish there. On the fifth day, we went to the colossal shopping centre in Faro half an hour away. I had a good experience with lots of fun and food! On the sixth day, we had some lovely family time with a giant pizza. On the last day, I wasn't that happy, but we could at least take the boat back home! Portugal was amazing and I will never forget about it.

Kaydon Colombo (9)

Byron Court Primary School, Wembley

The Incredible Diary Of... My First Day At School

Dear Diary,

It was my first day at school today and it was terrible! Kids were screaming, shouting, crying and, worst of all, I was bullied!

They were big seventeen-year-olds and they called me, "Four-eyes, fat lip Barbie!" Who calls someone Barbie when they're a boy?

Well, after my morning lessons and appalling break times, at the end of the day, I saw a boy just like me. Not in appearance, but in personality. I went up to him and noted, "It's not been a great day for me."

He replied, "Me neither." I told him that my name is Bob. His name was William.

This was my opportunity, "I'll meet you at the dinner hall tomorrow." After that, my first friend was made!

Aryan Kai Patel (10)
Byron Court Primary School, Wembley

The Incredible Diary Of... The Rotten Brat

Dear Diary,

Today, it's my twelfth birthday and Mum and Dad got me a 100 inch TV with a free iPhone XS. My mum does people's make-up and my dad sells cars. I'm sure they have more money than they need.

In school, I'm part of the gossip group with all the cool and rich popular girls. When they need my phone number, I say that I'm out of battery and can't add them. I forgot to mention that my name is Zelda. My name means strong, powerful and it's nerdy. I hate my name! I wanted to be called Nicky. My mum is always encouraging me to appreciate things, but all I can appreciate is my bed. I'm a bright student, I just get As in every class. I'm the best student in any class!

Rumessa Arif (10)

Byron Court Primary School, Wembley

The Amazing Day For Me

Dear Diary,

I am writing about the most exciting day! First, I went in the taxi to the airport with my mummy, daddy, little brother, nani and nana. Then, we went on the huge plane and after, we went on a big bus. After, we went to the hotel. It was amazing with lots of fun pools. When we were in our hotel, we sorted all our stuff.

We then went to have our lunch and we were excited because we were going to get changed and play in the pool. While we were in the pool with Nani and Nana, Mummy and Daddy got us some ice cream and they got chips too, they were yummy. After, we got changed and we had dinner and it was very good. Finally, we went to sleep in our massive bed.

Riya Hirani (7)
Byron Court Primary School, Wembley

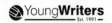
The Incredible Diary Of... A Lame Kid

Dear Diary,

Usually, Dad's always nagging me to go to school, but not now... it's the summer holidays! But it all went wrong. Mum came in and said, "Pack your bags, we're going to Disneyland!" All of a sudden, Rehan started crying because he wanted to go to Grandma's house but Mum had already bought the tickets. No one would want to go to Grandma's, she's so boring.

The taxi was here and I didn't think Mum would make any surprise holidays. Well, we went to the airport and guess what? Mum forgot the tickets! She wouldn't go back to get them because the flight was in two minutes! So, we ended up going to Grandma's house.

Zayan Akhtar (9)

Byron Court Primary School, Wembley

The Diary Of Marrie

Dear Diary,

I have had a hard time in my new school. I've had to find new friends and start from zero. Last Monday, I had to introduce myself. I was obviously shy and couldn't do it. I muttered, "Hello," slowly but clearly.

When it was break time, I went to three girls that seemed nice. "Hi," said a girl that claimed to be Sara.

"Hello," said Tiffany and Clara.

After that, I felt joy inside me. Now, I've got used to the class clowns and always do my best on tests, but I hate the food, so I always bring packed lunches. Oh, I also get sad and mad if my friends bail on me...

Erika Fernandes (8)

Byron Court Primary School, Wembley

The Incredible Diary Of...

Dear Diary,

I went to school with my friend, Zion. She is a Girls' Club leader! She is so bossy. Sometimes, when she argues with me, she cries and I cry, then everyone follows her and I'm left with no one. It's not fair that everyone bothers me and they make me feel bad about myself and, when I tell the teacher, it makes the situation worse. Then, Zion feels like nothing will happen, but I feel like she doesn't know how I feel. Every day, if it's not Zion's way, she'll cry out loud. When we talk it out properly, she is fine and we're happy. Then, the next day, she's nice.

Kamara Leigh-Bellot (8)
Byron Court Primary School, Wembley

The Incredible Diary Of... Zoya (The Girl And The Candy Alien)

Dear Diary,

Today, I was in my garden and I saw this magic hole. I went inside the catastrophic hole. There was a humongous alien who was furry, muscular and compassionate. I thought, *we'll be friends because the alien looks friendly!*

I was scared and amazed at the same time, but the alien was curious. We felt hungry and ordered some food. The alien liked milkshakes and I wanted chocolate. We were arguing about what food we should get, so we said we'd get a chocolate milkshake and we drank all of it. I then went back to my garden. It was the most incredible adventure in my life!

Zoya Butt (9)

Byron Court Primary School, Wembley

Am I Alive?

Dear Diary,

I can't believe that I'm alive, but I'm happy that I am. Sorry Diary, I just can't think, I'm heartbroken. A volcano erupted and my mum, dad and I escaped, but what about the others? What about them? Mum is trying very hard to reassure me that everything is fine.

Right now, I'm in a hotel in Rome. Sasho, my dog, is okay and is on my lap right now. She's panicking about the eruption too. I can't stop thinking about it. What about my friend, Laura? Is she alright? Oh my! I'll go to sleep at least, that way, I'll calm down...

Emily Ann Delchev (10)

Byron Court Primary School, Wembley

The Incredible Diary Of... Mario Kart

Dear Diary,

I've been trying to get a star in 50cc to get Baby Daisy. There'll be gold trophies and stars. There are eight cups, you need to get gold trophies and stars to get them. I'm trying to get all the stars and trophies on 50cc, then I'll get Baby Daisy!

Dear Diary,

I've been playing for two days. I'm surprised. I needed stars and trophies in 100cc. Luckily, I managed to get golden trophies and stars in less than two days and I got Bowser Jr! My next target is to get Dry Bowser.

Jenna Alfadhl (8)

Byron Court Primary School, Wembley

The Incredible Diary Of...

Dear Diary,

I have had the best day ever! This morning, I woke up, got dressed and packed ready for Scout Camp. I was going camping with my best friends, Edith and Gabriella, and I was so excited. First, I had to go to the Scout Hut to meet the leaders because the mini buses were there and the parents didn't know where the destination was.

Everyone was already there. We were all set to go. The journey was really long but when we finally got there, we did the most exciting thing ever - we did zip wire which was amazing! You went really high and even hit the trees (which wasn't very fun to me) and when Gary Petri (the most disgusting boy that is really called Bogey Fingers), got stuck on the zip wire, it was the funniest thing I have ever seen, but they got him down eventually. Next, I did crate stacking. It's where you stack crates as high as you can while standing on them. It was a little bit scary but so much fun. To end the day, we got to go in the shop. I bought an owl key ring and a wood key ring.

Finally, it was time to go home which was a shame as we were having such a good time. We shared snacks and goodies on the journey home.

I would love to do this all again with my friends another day.

Amelia Rose Stoddart (9)

Laleham CE Primary School, Laleham

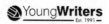
The Incredible Diary Of...

Dear Diary,

"Come, Pepper!" the lady called to her granddaughter. The lady would always bring Pepper down to the park and I would watch her, thinking, *why can't I have a family like Pepper?* Today was different. Today was the day when I had an opportunity to be a film star and get out of this ridiculous box in the park (Hollywood). You must have heard of Steven Spielberg. You know, the famous director who always shouts 'action!' at the top of his voice? His daughter, Sasha, came to my park! I was so excited that I started to bark to grab her attention. Looking shocked, she turned around and her eyes bulged. "Now *that* is film material!" She walked up to me and positioned me in her arms. I looked over my shoulder and saw Steven Spielberg, cameras and lights surrounding him. Sasha placed me down on a white sheet. She bent down and whispered in my ear, "Now, all you have to do is show off your flying skills!" I did as she said and, with direction from Steve, I flew in the air, my wings gracefully flapping with the wind. My dream has finally come true and I'm sure my adventures of being a film star will continue!

Ellie Ayoub (10)

Laleham CE Primary School, Laleham

Messi In Space

Dear Diary,

Today, the worst thing happened to me (Messi). It was a normal day and I had no football matches to do, so I went to the pub to have a pint of beer. All of a sudden, the TV turned on by itself and a man called Zidane said, "We are looking for some players to come to St Mary's football stadium. Those players are: Messi, Ronaldo, Mbappé, Neymar, Buffon, Pelé, Kanté, Chiellini, Ramos, Hummels and Griezmann."

Suddenly, we were all transported to the football stadium! Zidane explained that aliens were going to invade the planet. We spent a stressful couple of hours training, then we finally made the journey into the space stadium.

We were so scared. We knew that if we lost, our planet would be destroyed. Our team was called Galaxy 11. It was the first couple of minutes and I scored. It was one-nil to us!

It was then their kick-off and they had got the ball halfway up the pitch and Volgax (their captain) and Griezmann came in with the tackle and it was a penalty but to us. We scored. Two-nil! The planet was saved and we were all heroes!

Tay Brander (10)

Laleham CE Primary School, Laleham

The Incredible Diary Of...

Dear Diary,

Today, it was another boring day in my owner's head, or was it? By the way, I am a brain. I control everything my human does. Okay, so I kind of own my human instead of him owning me.

I was going to school. My lovely, happy school. We (my friends and I) were doing all the usual lessons: maths, English, science, PE and geography. Then, we had a break. And that's when it all happened...

Bang! My head went bang. It split open and I came running out. You might be thinking, how this can happen, well, I'll let you in on a little secret. I am a wizard! "Does anyone have a brain I can use?" I asked. "Wait, I *am* one. Hahaha! Why is nobody is laughing?"

Creak! The metallic blue school gates ripped open. "I am Voldemort. Bow down to me!" shouted Voldemort.

While my buddies were screaming and running around in circles like headless chickens, I pulled out my wand, ready to duel with the evildoer. "Avada Kedavra!" screamed Voldemort.

"Sectumsempra," I spoke. Streaks of power burst out of the wooden sticks. With a blinding light, the villain was turned into ash!

Joshua Jones (10)
Laleham CE Primary School, Laleham

The Incredible Diary Of...

Dear Diary,

This was the best adventure I've ever had! Today, I was so mad, just because I didn't get my favourite meal - fish and chips! Meow! I had never been away from home before. I was eager to explore the world to witness the fascination that everyone is always excited about.

Curiously, I stumbled upon a few men nearby and children packing weird suitcases and cramming them into a small car. Without thinking, I leapt into it. I heard the children whispering about a holiday to France. *That's a long way from America!* I thought.

While clearing stringent checks at the airport, I sat as still as a statue; everyone thought I was a toy. I made it through!

After the turbulent journey (it was quite scary), I was in France. Everyone spoke a strange language which I worked out was French. I didn't know what to do, so I copied other people. I saw some cats playing so I jumped in.

"Bonjour!" exclaimed a cat. Feeling sad, I turned my head and lay down in a corner.

Luckily, a girl picked me up and whispered, "Let's go back home!" So here I am, snuggled up in my little home again.

Aarya Thombre (10)
Laleham CE Primary School, Laleham

The Incredible Diary Of...

Dear Diary,

Guess what happened today? I went on an adventurous journey to a land I had never seen before! I was having a normal day until two avatars (that were creepy) came up to me and picked me up as I'm a pen.

As they took me to their flying machine, I felt butterflies in my stomach thinking, *what are they going to do with me?* On their screen, it came up with, 'Welcome spies'.

"They're spies!" I said to myself, confused.

Two hours later, we had finally stopped.

There were mythical creatures and things I had never seen before. It felt like I was dreaming. I couldn't believe what I was seeing! As I was looking at everything, we went out to explore. Suddenly, I saw a giant boat that had crashed and sunk to the bottom of the sea. Suddenly, there was a big noise. *Bang!* "Argh!" I shouted as me and the spies were sprinting as fast as we could to the machine.

Later that day, we finally made it back to the normal world. It was a great day but it was nerve-wracking.

But the thing I want to know is, why did they take me on that journey?

Jessica Thomson (10)
Laleham CE Primary School, Laleham

The Playoff Finals

Dear Diary,

As soon as I woke up, I was ready for the big day at Wembley. It was finally the 26th of May. When I got on the coach to Wembley, my heart was thumping. Next thing I knew was that I was training. I was really happy to play in the final as I am only eighteen years old.

As soon as we were done, we walked to the tunnel and walked out. I was really happy but also nervous as there were 19.9 million people watching Fulham vs Aston Villa! My teammates (Tom Cairney and Mitrovic) were encouraging me to play well, so that gave me confidence.

When we got the kick-off, we started really well. Over the next twenty-two minutes, Cairney passed the ball to Sessegnon and... what a goal! It was one-nil to Fulham.

Seventy-eight minutes later, the final whistle came. Finally, Fulham had won against Aston Villa! Everyone was jumping and happy. When it was time to lift up the trophy, everyone was so excited, we went back down and got medals and celebrated. We were so happy to win the playoff final. We were also getting £200,000 to buy some players for the next exciting season.

Andrew Kluth (9)

Laleham CE Primary School, Laleham

Kylian Mbappé's Diary

Dear Diary,

It was the big day, the World Cup final! France vs Croatia. I was only nineteen and I would be playing in a World Cup final!

In pre-match training, our manager started with some boring running drills. Next, we moved into an enjoyable seven-aside match. The score at the end was eleven-ten to my team, I scored six goals and I got five assists!

Six hours later, the French and Croatian fans made their way to their seats to watch the training drills. I felt proud and nervous. Our manager called us to get ready.

Thirty minutes later, we lined up in the tunnel. Next to me stood the Croatian players including Modric and Mandzukic.

The two teams started to walk out of the tunnel. The game kicked off and we opened the scoring with an own goal. One-nil. Ivan Perisic scored a wonderful volley. One-one. My best friend, Antoine Griezmann, made it two-one to France.

Ten minutes later, Pogba made it three-one to France with a fantastic finish. I made it four-one. I felt over the moon. Mandzukic made it four-two but it wasn't enough. France were champions! It was the best day ever!

Joseph Nicol (10)
Laleham CE Primary School, Laleham

The Incredible Diary Of... A Shoe

Dear Diary,

I'd been having the worst days of my life! My owner (Kate) was in the woods for a short stroll with her family, when she stepped in a gooey, muddy puddle. That's when my life became a misery.

However, the next day, everything changed when Kate decided to go to the park with her sister and brother (Emma and Callan) and me. When we got there, Kate was allowed to wander around by herself. Walking along the path, Kate's eyes fixed upon a beautiful, bright, golden door covered in emerald-green vines, she couldn't stop staring at it. It's amazing how she never looks at me that way... Suddenly, Kate opened the door and stepped inside, and there, standing before us, was a magical kingdom full of wonder, fairies and best of all *unicorns!*

Kate and I were having a great time meeting everyone until Emma called for her sister and our fun was over, so we said goodbye to everyone. I wish I was allowed to smuggle a unicorn home with me! But I wasn't, so that was that.

I know I can call this the *best day ever!*
PS My name is Lacy the shoe!

Kate Kriel (10)

Laleham CE Primary School, Laleham

N'Golo Kanté: Chelsea And The French Magician!

Dear Diary,

It was another ordinary day in Russia, but tomorrow was the World Cup final 2018. I was playing with France.

My friend, Mbappé, gave me a call at nine o'clock. I went to bed with joy and anxiety.

When I woke up to go to the famous Luzhniki Stadium, I saw all my teammates in their amazing France kits. After all their positive words, my butterflies went away. My manager, Henri Michel, also gave some amazing tactics to our whole team. When we were going through the tunnel, I was only hearing fans shouting, "Come on France!" As the kick-off was taken, my butterflies went away. I looked up the pitch, *wow!* We scored. I cheered really loud, "Yes!"

I went to celebrate with Mbappé and Pogba. It happened again, a goal, but for Croatia...

Ivan Perisic scored again. But it was an own goal. Two-nil. I passed it to Griezmann and I got the assist. Goal but for France! Three-one. Again. Four-one. No! They scored but it was still four-two!

The whistle blew and I cheered, yeah! I lifted the World Cup and nearly cried with excitement!

Kenny Nugent

Laleham CE Primary School, Laleham

The Incredible Diary Of...

Dear Diary,

Today has been the most peculiar day. When I woke up, I got dressed and went down to the Quidditch pitch for the Quidditch match.

When I had reached the pitch, instead of the regular Quidditch stands, I saw four colourful rockets. "What's going on?" I asked.

"Today's Quidditch match is on the moon," said Snape, who was walking towards the shiny green and silver rocket that obviously represented Slytherin.

Very excited, I walked towards the red and gold rocket and stepped into it. It was much bigger on the inside than it looked on the outside. I thought this would be a lot different compared to a normal Quidditch match.

Next minute, I heard Dumbledore shout, "Three, two, one, blast off!" The rockets zoomed upwards at top speed.

Is this really happening? I thought. *Am I really going to the moon?*

As the rockets were so fast, it took no less than three hours to get there. Before I got out, I used a special charm with my wand to allow me to breathe in space. When I got out, I was determined that I was going to win...

Oscar Preece (10)

Laleham CE Primary School, Laleham

The Incredible Diary Of...

Dear Diary,

It started off as a normal day but then, I saw a bright yellow light, then another and, pretty soon, there were thousands of yellow lights all around me. I knew what it was almost instantly... Aliens! I ran for my life.

As I anxiously ran, I could hear my heart racing. I felt a trickle of perspiration drop down my cheek. I could hear, "Lg, lg, lg, Venus and Mars. Lg, lg, lg." I thought, *they must be from Venus and Mars!*

Then, I saw a beaming light shining on a black and white cat. Suddenly, the cat got sucked up through the beam, screeching, and was pulled into the UFO. An alien beam narrowly missed me as I dodged out of the way.

I thought I was safe inside a clothes shop, sheltered from the beams, when a lime-green alien knocked down the doors, using its feet, and entered the shop. I tried to speak their language, "Lg, lg, lg, go away, lg, lg, lg." Luckily, it worked! Several more aliens came and I told them all to go away and so, they all went back to Venus and Mars! Finally, I rushed home to meet my grey husky dog, Tom.

Luca Warren

Laleham CE Primary School, Laleham

The Diary Of A Raindrop

Dear Diary,

I was drifting around with my friends when the sun came out. We all thought it would be nice because the sun hadn't come out in ages. But then, I started to rise into the sky with some of my friends! We thought we were going to die and may be separated from our families forever; we were rising closer to the sun!

After three minutes, we were gathered so closely together that we formed a cloud. We were gliding through the air like a bird. We were having so much fun soaring through the sky sightseeing, when we suddenly dropped! I was plummeting towards the Arctic Ocean.

Once I landed in the sea, I started drifting towards Iceland. Well, it wasn't as pretty as I'd thought as a volcano (Eldfell) was erupting with bright red magma. There were noises, thick ash filled the sky, boulders were flying out of the volcano and crushing the houses, ash covered the buildings! There were tubes sticking in the water and sucking up my friends. I tried to get out of there as fast as I could, but I got sucked up into the tube and squirted out right at the exploding volcano...

Ryan Hutt (10)

Laleham CE Primary School, Laleham

The Incredible Diary Of...

Dear Diary,

Today, some people tried to dig into me! I didn't know what to do but what could I do? Just let them keep on digging? They were digging into my red-hot core! What were they trying to do? Kill me? I quietly asked my friend, Mars, "What can I do?" Loudly, Mars answered, "How should I know? It's never happened to me before."

"Okay," I replied, then I continued spinning around the sun. I was sweating. It's really hard work in case you didn't know. If you don't believe me, you try spinning around for 365 days with no break. Now, back to explaining. I tried to shake them off again until they started making stuff on me. They had blocks on me. I thought, *should I make a massive volcano? No*, I thought. I was curious. I wanted to see what they would do. If they were to hurt me, I would stop them at once. I said to Mars, "They seem to be building on me."

Mars answered, "That's so weird, shall we ask Moon? After all, he is the wisest."

"Yes," I agreed and faded away slowly with Mars...

Tristan Thomas

Laleham CE Primary School, Laleham

Bob Goes Skateboarding

Dear Diary,

Today, I had a crazy day because a skateboard fell from the Earth. This morning, I woke up after my neighbour started playing his sea drums. After having my sea bites, I realised something peculiar was in my washing. It was hard and colourful and not normal.

I swam over to it and used my two little fins to push it down to the sandy seabed below. It was a sort of game - something the humans used. It was a huge miracle for a tortoise to find human belongings and I definitely wanted to try it out. Although I was a different shape to human beings, I knew I could.

Once I'd fitted the object safely into the creamy seabed, I jumped on it and used my strong flippers to push it slowly forwards. Really, it was not that stable. It jiggled, it wobbled, it shook and vibrated. It quivered, it shuddered, it throbbed and pulsed. It felt like a body was inside of it, only I knew it couldn't be true. I couldn't control this beastly item. It felt impossible! I don't even think I can to this moment. Now if it wasn't for hope, I could have given up.

Aishah Kola-Olukotun (10)

Laleham CE Primary School, Laleham

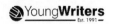

The Incredible Diary Of...

Dear Diary,

You will never believe it! As I am a plane, every day is tiring for me. Get ready to hear about the best journey ever! It all started on a hot summer's day at Heathrow Airport. It was my time to shine as the airport was filled with visitors. Soon, hundreds of people would start boarding me. I always felt nervous when travelling to different countries. Eventually, everyone started coming on. Nerves started tingling inside me. The pilot announced that we were going to Canada. You can never be too sure about what might happen along the way. Finally, I took off on the amazing journey to Canada, which made me fill with nerves. Gusts of freezing wind flew past me. The sky filled to the brim with dark clouds. I knew something was not right. The wind started getting stronger and stronger so I started shaking about! All I could do was not give up.

A few hours later, I was over the middle of the sea and rain started falling down. Canada was in the distance, which meant nothing would stop me.

Gently, I landed safely onto the runway. It was the best day ever!

Zachary Buckle
Laleham CE Primary School, Laleham

Super Dog!

Dear Diary,

I must be the fastest dog in the world! Today, I ran around the whole world, doing my favourite thing - chasing squirrels. It began as a normal but beautiful sunny day and I was out for a walk in the park when I spotted a squirrel that looked brilliant for chasing. So what do you think I did? Chase it of course! Now, when I started this pursuit, I never realised how much stamina squirrels have!

I was so excited and I couldn't stop myself from leaping over the fence, into the golden fields beyond. Soon, I began to worry about my owner and the fact that I was completely and utterly lost. The urge to run was just too strong and I thought, *I can't turn back now anyway, I'll never find my way home from here!*

Suddenly, I felt something change - I was sprinting on water! I thought I must be a super dog because, within seconds, I was past the Eiffel Tower, Taj Mahal and the pyramids in Egypt. Before I knew it, I was back in the park I'd started in. My owner seemed really relieved to see me, but I was extremely confused. How did I do that?

Katie McCummiskey (10)
Laleham CE Primary School, Laleham

The Incredible Diary Of...

Dear Diary,

Today, I woke up in the fruit bowl. It was someone's birthday, but I didn't know whose. The family left to go to LegoLand for two days, so I jumped out of the fruit bowl, walked over to the kitchen, climbed up to the blender and started to make my favourite drink - a chocolate smoothie! I put in chopped up chocolate, marshmallow sweets, chocolate milk and blended it all together. Once it had finished mixing, I gulped it all down into my starving stomach and finished off with some chocolate Oreos.

With my tummy full, I decided to watch BBC News on TV. I pressed the 'on' button on what I thought was the remote, but it was the CCTV footage remote and I saw two criminals, armed with crowbars, trying to get into the house! I looked outside and saw that it was true. There were criminals trying to break in!

I found some things that I could use to set up some traps. I attached some string across the floor so they would trip over. I put a bat up high so it would fall on their heads and knock them out. I then called 999 for help...

Mylo Stansbury (10)
Laleham CE Primary School, Laleham

83

Twinkle And The Pet Shop Raid

Dear Diary,

You won't believe what happened today! I was casually sleeping amongst my bedding with the sun on my face when I heard the sound of motorbikes... I wearily opened my eyes to see my besties - Sparky and Harry the guinea pigs! They were excitedly squeaking to wake me. "Hey, Twinkle! Would you, Scamp and Pepper like to come to the pet shop with us?"

Of course, I said yes. Who wouldn't? "But how are we going to get there? Scamp and I are only hamsters and we don't want to be squished!" Then I had an idea! Sparky opened my cage and I crawled out and into my feisty roommate's bedroom to find a Lego aeroplane.

We probably looked mad - a dog on roller skates, two hamsters in a Lego aeroplane and guinea pigs on flying cloud motorbikes!

At last! Pet's Corner! I dashed straight into the small pets section with Scamp. Before my eyes was the most beautiful thing ever, apart from my owner... A 90g bag of sunflower seeds! I tucked in. Soon, my belly was full and so were my cheeks. It had been the best pet shop raid in history!

Olivia Jones

Laleham CE Primary School, Laleham

The Super Duper Psychic

Dear Diary,

This week was the coolest week. I was on a great adventure with my psychic, Joe. He wasn't really the most helpful boy of the week... Anyway, let me start. I was at the England military base and my boss called me in for a mission. He said that someone had stolen the most precious material in the world - a diamond. I just don't mean any diamond, I mean the Queen's! It was all over the news, but why would someone do that? Well... we needed to find out who it was. So how would I start? *By asking the Queen,* I thought.

I was standing in Buckingham Palace with my partner, asking the Queen questions about the crime. She said that he had black hair and blue eyes, then we looked at the cameras. I recognised that guy! The trusty psychic was not the trusty psychic. He started running, I started running. The chase had begun, we were both in our cars.

He was way ahead but I knew where he was going, he was racing to our top-secret den. He suddenly stopped, I stopped. "I've caught you red-handed!" There was nowhere to go...

Henry Michael Peter Sharman

Laleham CE Primary School, Laleham

The Day I Met Twinkle

Dear Diary,

Today was the most eventful day of my life! This morning, when I was strolling through the woods, I reached a place which seemed like a magical wonderland. I didn't think anyone had ever seen anything like that before!

Just as I was about to leave, I heard a gentle ring of a bell, it was almost like it was calling my name. As I walked a little closer to the hypnotising sound, I trod towards a creature. I realised it was a... unicorn! Was it fake? Was I the first person to see this unicorn? I took my bag off my back and I took my sweets out (doughnuts, lollipops and chocolate cake.)

After I'd fed all my sweets to the unicorn, I named it Twinkle and I took her to my home. I'd never realised there was a pen at my home. I'm a princess so I live in a castle! My mum, the queen, was shocked and never knew such a creature was alive. I put her in her shiny, cute, rainbow stable. Now, she sneaks out sometimes and sneaks doughnuts and sweets into her pen, but I still love her and that's what makes Twinkle her amazing self!

Abigail Francis (9)

Laleham CE Primary School, Laleham

The Horror Park

Dear Diary,

Today, I had a terrifying day. It started off as a normal day until my dad sent me to my bedroom for apparently terrorising my evil sister. In my football-style bedroom, I got so bored that I did something very bad. So, you know I've got a magic diary and I promised I'd never use it again? I did. I used it to go to the coolest theme park ever!

Anyway, when I got there, my parents let me go on this haunted house ride. When I got there, I almost regretted it but went in nonetheless.

Inside, it was dark with small red lights dotted around. Creepy noises echoed around the room and frightening skeletons limped towards me.

After a while, I headed back but couldn't find the way! Although I searched for around an hour, I just couldn't find the way. Suddenly, I heard a creaking noise. The park gates were closing! I reached a dead end but saw some steps, so I headed up and paused when I heard talking. As I put my ear up to the door, they seemed to talk in a strange language. Suddenly, the door opened and zombies grabbed me...

Megan Williams (10)
Laleham CE Primary School, Laleham

The Incredible Diary Of...

Dear Diary,

As I walked into the Bubletown stadium, I saw the best long distance runner in the world - Mo Farah. Today was going to be the best! One minute until Mo Farah tried to beat the world record time for the Bubletown Marathon. Just before the race, I shook his hand but I was faster than normal...

Then, I was standing shaking a little boy's hand... *I* was Mo Farah! That meant I was going to run the Bubletown Marathon and try and beat the world record time. I am good at running but I'd never done the marathon before. The starting official called all the racers over and told us the rules. After explaining the rules, we were all lined up. "On your marks, get set, go!"

With a bang, he shot the pistol and we were off. I had to go at a slow pace but it was different, I was going faster than normal! At first I thought I was dreaming but then I remembered that I was Mo Farah. After a while, I saw the finish line. Finally, I had made it and the time was 1:43:13, a new world record. That was the best day ever!

Alexander Wigmore (9)

Laleham CE Primary School, Laleham

The Incredible Diary Of...

Dear Diary,

Today, I woke up to a doughnut on my bedside table. I ignored it and strolled downstairs. In my breakfast bowl was the same doughnut, so I decided to make pancakes for breakfast instead. Once I was ready to get dressed and brush my teeth, I went upstairs to the bathroom and, in the sink, was the pink-iced doughnut I'd seen downstairs and on my bedside table! It was following me! I was creeped out.

I finished in the bathroom and went to my bedroom. On the shelf was the exact, same doughnut from before! I got dressed while keeping an eye on that yummy doughnut. I thought it was my brother joking around, but he would usually be asleep or eating breakfast...

Nothing happened throughout the day other than the doughnut following me. It was dinnertime and we decided to go out for dinner. We drove to the restaurant and ordered the food. On the table was the pink-iced doughnut! I ate all my food and was ready for pudding, so I decided to eat the doughnut that had followed me all day. I started to float up into the air...

Rosie Rayner-Kent (10)

Laleham CE Primary School, Laleham

The Incredible Diary Of...

Dear Diary,

Today has been the most eventful day of my life! When it was dark, a few rumbles shook my remote island. Not many people woke up, but I did - I always wake up at little things like that - but today, it wasn't a little thing, it was a huge thing. My island was in danger! The volcano was shaking. I raised the alarm as I knew this was dangerous...

Soon, the whole of my island was alive at three o'clock in the morning. Emergency vehicles flew through the streets of Hiemaey with sirens blaring, making sure that everyone was out of bed to escape the eruption. I sprinted down to the docks - everyone else was going there. All the boats were there. There had been a storm last night and it had been too dangerous to fish, so we suddenly had means of escape. Just at that moment, a huge roar started to shake the ground...

A fiery inferno rose out of the dreaded, rocky mountain. Suddenly, it went quiet. Then, the Mayor told everyone to get on a boat. I never thought that so many people could get onto a boat but we did. I was safe!

Joey Walker (10)

Laleham CE Primary School, Laleham

The Incredible Diary Of...

Dear Diary,

I'm Sparky the guinea pig. I live with my owners, Isobel and Thomas. My cage buddy is my sister, Harriet (but all our friends call her Harry). I'm going to tell you about a day in the life of me. This diary is about the day me and my friends raided the pet store.

Me and Harry heard our owner (Isobel) say that her mum and her brother (Thomas) were going away with her on something called a holiday (what's that?) When they left, their dad gave us cucumber. He told us he would be at work all day. We drove to our friend's house on our secret cloud motorbikes.

When we got there, we went upstairs to wake up Twinkle and Scamp. We went to town to where the pet store is located. We probably looked really weird to the humans (that was because we were guinea pigs riding on clouds, a hamster in a Lego aeroplane and a dog on roller skates!) We got to the pet store for the raid. We all got what we wanted and headed home. We were back in the cage before Dad came back from work. What an awesome day! *Squeak!*

Isobel Watson
Laleham CE Primary School, Laleham

The Incredible Diary Of...

Dear Diary,

Today, I had the proudest moment of my life! It started off like a regular day - it was my owner, Jess', seventh birthday! As it was her birthday, I wanted to do something special; I wanted to bake her some specially baked cookies!

Once Jess had left for school, I yapped happily as I wagged my fluffy tail around. Soon after, I found her cookbook and I got all the ingredients (which was hard for me as I am only a small, little Pomeranian).

As I reached up for the chocolate chips, a large bag of flour tipped over my head (the chocolate chips were safe). I saw my appearance reflected in the oven door - I looked like a ghost!

As soon as I had gathered all my ingredients, I started mixing the flour with some ingredients. Soon after, I put the cookies in the oven. I had already licked all the bowls! Excitedly, I rushed the cookies out of the oven and carefully decorated the warm biscuits.

Suddenly, the door swung wide open and Jess saw the beautiful cookies and knew they were from me and gave me a big hug!

Leah Warmington
Laleham CE Primary School, Laleham

To Be A Football Player

Dear Diary,

I got up and had breakfast. Then, I got into my car and went to the Brentford training ground and trained for the FA Cup final. We got onto the bus and were on our way to Wembley! I was so excited to get there. When we got there, we entered the stadium and went into the changing room. We got changed into our away kit and went onto the pitch. I walked out onto the pitch - I was so happy! I saw the cup and I really wanted to pick it up and take it back to Brentford!

At half-time, we were one-nil up. I was so excited because at full time we won three-nil! I was lucky, I was allowed to pick up the trophy. I got to share that amazing moment with my fans. It was a special moment with my family, friends, teammates and fans and I felt I was going to cry. We all went back into the changing room cheering and showered. Then we got on the bus and took the FA Cup back to Brentford!

We spent the next week training to be ready for a championship match against Aston Villa - a big, fun, exciting game. We will probably win that match too!

Isaac Cook (10)

Laleham CE Primary School, Laleham

Any Tents Still Standing?

Dear Diary,

Today, I experienced an odd day involving tents blowing down and falling down hills! Today, I had an ordinary day (you could say) up until we came back from our hike. Let me start from the beginning.

It all started when, last night, I didn't get much sleep because my pillow in the tent was so uncomfortable. After I got dressed, we went playing until 8:30. When the leaders finally woke up, we had a delicious bacon roll and then we set foot on our five and a half hour hike.

As we left the campsite, we started off the day by walking up a very steep hill but, as it was windy, I fell. To start my day on a high, I said to myself, "Why get up?" So I started rolling down the hill, I felt happier already. When I finally got to the bottom, I carried on the path.

After five hours of walking, we finally got back to the entrance, but the wind was so strong that all of our tents had blown down and the gazebo had snapped! Unfortunately, the tents were unfixable so we had to go home. What an exciting, great day.

Gabriella Butler (10)

Laleham CE Primary School, Laleham

Fire Horse

Dear Diary,

This morning, I woke up and looked out my window to see a beautiful, beaming sunrise staring back at me. The sea was still and a magical feeling filled the air. I skipped out of my bedroom, down the stairs and onto the sandy shore. I walked forwards as the sand tickled my feet.

Out on the horizon, a glaring fire horse (standing tall and proud) was smiling at me. It bowed and it was gone. The salty spray blurred my vision. I rubbed my eyes. All that was left were three doves dancing on the wind. I put my foot out into the water and hummed a very joyful song.

All of a sudden, it was there, more angelic than ever, walking towards me - the fire horse! It spread its wings and galloped like a warrior towards the shore. It stopped in front of me. There was a peaceful silence that filled the air. My heart was filled with joy. The stallion bowed its head. I put my hand out to stroke it and it nuzzled its nose into my hand. Water came splashing up at us, covering both me and the horse in the water. The horse had vanished...

Ella Miller (10)
Laleham CE Primary School, Laleham

Rusty The Friendly Fox

Dear Diary,

Today was a nightmare! First, I woke up to the sound of the crazy cockerel on Seedhill Farm. After that, I went to find some scraps for my breakfast. The farmer was already up at this time so he could feed the cute, fluffy, spring ducklings. I smiled at their sweet, little cheeps. Unfortunately, the farmer had turned around and seen my smile. He thought I was being cunning! He chased me out so I didn't get any breakfast. After wandering back to my den, I sat down under the shade of a tree. I went without food for the whole day!

I was extremely lonely and, now that the farmer would not accept my presence on the farm, I couldn't bear watching the ducklings cheeping on their own. Feeling frustrated, I headed to find some food in the fields even though it was the evening. I knew the farmer was in bed by this time, but I noticed a strange, dark figure heading for the ducklings.

I growled and he stopped dead. This was not the farmer. It was a burglar and I had stopped him! Now, I am accepted at Seedhill Farm!

Aoife Grimwood (10)
Laleham CE Primary School, Laleham

Arsenal Win The Premier League

Dear Diary,

Today was the best day of my life! I scored the best goal ever against Tottenham. It was a league match - we were both on seventy-two points, coming first, and it was our last game this season. As I was warming up, I felt very nervous. Once we had finished warming up, we went into the tunnel to have a team talk. We went onto the pitch, we had the advantage as it was at our ground (Emirates Stadium), we also had kick-off.

We had a great start as Lacazette scored in the first ten minutes, but they nearly scored, but Leno managed to get a brilliant save. As soon as he booted it out his hands, the ref blew the whistle for half-time. We went into the tunnel and had a quick chat. Then, once finished, we went back out.

They had kick-off and scored in the eighty-seventh minute. We didn't give up, we kept going. I got the ball in the last few seconds. I knew the ref was going to blow the whistle so I smashed it up the pitch and managed to get an amazing goal. I slid over to the fans and celebrated with them!

Charlie Hobbs (10)
Laleham CE Primary School, Laleham

The Incredible Diary Of...

Dear Diary,

It was an amazing day! It was Christmas Eve. I was so excited for Christmas. I had even bought myself new pyjamas for the super special day. Although my brother was grumpy, my parents said that I could have more presents because I am six and he is sixteen!

It was 9pm and I was in my new pyjamas. I had hung my stocking on the end of my bed and I had laid milk and cookies on my table. Suddenly, I heard footsteps on the roof of my house. Could it be him? My heart was beating so fast. I could be one of the few lucky people to see the amazing Santa!

Just at that moment, I heard somebody munching my biscuits and then I knew he was here. I leapt out of bed and gave him a hug! Santa was so shocked but I was so happy. "What are you doing?" he bellowed.

"I heard you on my roof and I got so excited!" I replied.

"Well in that case, here is my present for you and don't tell anyone you saw me," he told me.
"Okay!" I said in excitement and Santa flew away.

Genevieve Hodge
Laleham CE Primary School, Laleham

The World Cup Final

Dear Diary,

Today was the most extraordinary day ever. It all started when me and my teammates got on the coach.

We finally arrived at Luzhiniki Stadium. As the captain, I said a few final words of encouragement before we jogged onto the pitch. That was it. That was the World Cup final and we were head-to-head with Croatia. As the referee blew his whistle, I felt proud. At half-time, the score was two-two and it was the closest match that I had ever been a part of.

The second half was yet again equal. That only meant one thing - extra time. Mbappé scored his third goal of the match and we were ahead for the first time. We were surely going to win now, but our celebration was called to a halt when, in the minutes of added time, Paul brought Luka Modri down in the penalty box. If they scored, we would be level yet again! Get in! I saved it and the whistle went as my teammates jumped onto me. I felt prouder than I ever had before - I captained France to victory! We are now the champions of the world!

Madeline Rose Evans (10)

Laleham CE Primary School, Laleham

The Incredible Diary Of...

Dear Diary,

It was another ordinary day in Italy for me. When I got out of my house, I was going to a meeting to see who'd stolen the crown jewels. As I drove off in my car to the conference, heaps of traffic arrived. Once I got there, I propelled my coat onto the hanger which careered through the window. I walked into the meeting, joyful to be there.

Twenty minutes later, I suggested splitting into groups in order to locate where the missing jewels were. We departed from the meeting to look. I was with James (personally, I didn't really know much about this guy but I guessed he was on our side). We walked over to this dark alleyway just near the Tower of Piza (oh sorry, I mean Pisa). There were these people yelling about jewels (I know, I'm quite curious about these things so I checked it out). I whispered to James about this as well.

I started to chase them and tried to overpower them, although they were extremely resilient because they were running rapidly. Then, we lost them...

Sam Dylan Mausolle (10)
Laleham CE Primary School, Laleham

The Incredible Diary Of...
Cristiano Ronaldo

Dear Diary,

We slowly got up, got ready and had breakfast. A few hours later, the Portugal team's bus came to take us to the Stade De France. On the bus, we sang all of Portugal's songs.

When we got there, we went straight to the dressing room and got changed. Then, we had our pre-match meal and went out onto the pitch to warm-up before the game. First, we had to do some running drills and stretches. Finally, we did a possession game.

We were in the dressing room, having our team talk. Our coach, Fernando Santos, went first. Then Nani went next, then me. I said, "We've done so well to get this far. One more win and we will go down in history!"

It was kick-off. Seven minutes in, I got the ball and Dimitri Payet fouled me. I was on the ground, screaming with agony. On the touchline, I tested my knee. After a few more tries on the pitch, I had to come off.

Later, Eder came on and scored the winner. At the

final whistle, there were tears in my eyes. We had finally won!

James White (10)
Laleham CE Primary School, Laleham

The Boy Who Went To Heaven

Dear Diary,

Today was the best day of my life, you will never believe what happened! So, the day started off with a normal morning - eating breakfast, getting changed you know, the usual. Suddenly, everything changed, a fire broke out in the kitchen! The flames danced around excitedly. How terrible it was watching everything burn in front of my eyes - all of my money, all of my photos, all gone forever. Unexpectedly, a bright sunbeam glared into my eyes. There were shiny buildings towering over me. Where was I? What had happened?

Strangely, I felt comfortable and better than I had ever felt before. As I looked down, I realised I was not on solid ground, I was standing on a cloud. Then, I knew I was in Heaven! My eyes flooded with tears. I was dead, I would never see my family and friends again! Suddenly, out of the corner of my eye, I noticed a familiar face - my grandad! The tears turned to laughter as we caught up about our lives. Then, I explained to my grandad my plan to return back to Earth...

Sam Robert Shepherd (10)

Laleham CE Primary School, Laleham

The Diary Of Spike

Dear Diary,

On a gloomy day in London, Harry Kane had just missed a penalty against Man City (that would have won them the match). I was so angry, I decided to go and steal his car! Since it was misty, it was a perfect day to steal something like a car. My plan was excellent. This would be my hardest mission yet and the most exciting!

This was also Mission 200. That meant, if I was successful, I got my ultra-badge. I thought, *this could be the best day of my life!* I would become a robber mentor for kids of all ages!

That night, I crept to Harry's house and destroyed the security cameras and climbed over the gate. I felt a rush of excitement and nervousness. The house was amazing and big. I felt so jealous because my house is not as fantastic as his. I approached the amazing vehicle and moved my hand along the smooth black car. I had to go into the house to get the keys. That would be easy enough for me. I got the keys and got the car. I got back to my awesome house in a flash!

Jacob Courtney Maycock-Prime (9)
Laleham CE Primary School, Laleham

The Incredible Diary Of... Rosa Parks

Dear Diary,

Today, a lady came into my shop. She rudely thrust a dress at me and said, "Don't you dare handle my dress too much or you'll be in for it, Rosa Parks!"
I hate it when white people think they're better than us. It's unfair in 1955...
I decided to take a little breather, escape the unfairness of the cruel world. I locked the door behind me - there was no point coming back.
Walking around, enjoying the fresh dusk air, a bus drove past. It was empty so no white people would bother me. I hopped on, wishing we would drive away to a carefree world. But we didn't.
More white people joined.
As they piled on, a lady wearing a dark purple dress came up to me and spat, "Move, I want to sit here and I will."
"No. I would like to sit here. Go and sit elsewhere."
It was then she went to ask the driver for assistance. I was ever so nervous, but I had to stand up for what was right! He called the police and I was taken to prison...

Emily Isla Byrne (9)
Laleham CE Primary School, Laleham

The Girl And The Crystal Cave

Dear Diary,

Today, I had the most exciting and scary day ever because, this morning, I woke up and I was in a crystal cave! I heard a scary noise, it came from the end of the cave (I was terrified). I walked to the end of the cave and saw a blue crystal monster with red eyes! Luckily he was asleep, but then I stepped on a twig and it made a crack. He woke up and came running at me!

Suddenly, a pink and purple monster grabbed me and saved my life. He took me to his cave and gave me a blanket because it was freezing cold like ice down in the mystery cave. This was amazing - he took me out of his cave and took me to the crystal palace and took me to the queen of the kingdom of crystals. She was wearing a snow-white cloak with a crown made of crystals. She was the most beautiful monster ever. She said to me, "What are you doing down in here?"

I replied with, "I don't know, I woke up here!"

She let me stay at her palace until we found a way out.

Bethany Anderson

Laleham CE Primary School, Laleham

The Incredible Diary Of...

Dear Diary,

Yesterday was the craziest! My owner (Emily) accidentally left my cage door open. I knew I should not have walked out, but I could not help it. What was it like out there? I had to go look!

A few minutes later, I was climbing up the stairs; I had always wanted to see the human world. It was very hard to get up the stairs but I knew I could do it! In a couple of seconds, I was up. The house was silent! "Where is everyone?" I questioned to myself. I remembered that Emily had said in the past that they were going on holiday. Yes! It was time to go on an adventure.

First, I decided to look in the room on my left. What was that pink blob sitting on the floor and that black square on top of the white rectangle? I felt very confused! I climbed up another set of stairs, why were there two rooms? These were bedrooms I realised. I got on a bed and ended up falling asleep!

Emily Walles (9)

Laleham CE Primary School, Laleham

The Incredible Diary Of...

Dear Diary,

It was another old day. I was practising football when I kicked the ball over the wall. Great. As I climbed to get it, I saw it glow. "Wow, that was cool! How did that happen?"

As I touched the ball, my hand glowed like magic. It sucked me in... I was playing in the Champions League against Tottenham! It was nil-nil at halftime so I needed to do my magic in the last half of the match. It was open to me. I went to the left side of the goal and scored! There were still five minutes left. I shot from the halfway line and I scored. Goal! What a goal, yes we won the game two-nil. I was crowned man of the match and won the golden boot!

Brentford had won the Champions League, what a feeling. Sadly, I had to go home. I held the ball up and *zoom* I was off. When I got home, I went straight to my room. My mum said, "Where were you?"

Josh Giblett (9)

Laleham CE Primary School, Laleham

The Incredible Diary Of...

Dear Diary,

Today, I had an amazing day and I can't wait to tell you. It was exhilarating!

I was rolling in the mud (as usual) when I felt a gust of wind pick me up and it flew me over the ocean, all the way to Canada! I started wandering around when I saw a field full of mud. I was speechless! As the field was coming closer, a gust of wind came and blew me away.

As I was just getting up, I noticed I was in France! I thought to myself, *why does it always have to happen to me?* I went and got a croissant and it was delicious. As I was walking, I saw the horror of my fellow species being cooked! *Bacon!* I was horrified. Suddenly, a gust of wind picked me up and blew me to Russia!

In Russia, I got some food to eat, luckily there was no bacon. I saw some Russian dolls. And that was my day. I am exhausted!

Lewis Hyman (9)

Laleham CE Primary School, Laleham

The Incredible Diary Of...

Dear Diary,

I've not had a great time at Scout Camp. When we got to the campsite, I was so excited for the weekend ahead. I was wrong. We had to put our tent up *in the rain!* But I wouldn't let that get my hopes down, I mean, it was just a bit of rain. Anyway, when Gabriella, Amelia and I had finished (putting up Mr Horrific), we went to get our stuff and spent *half an hour unpacking!* Wow, okay. When we had done messing stuff up, we all went outside and had hot chocolate (which was disgusting) and went to bed. *And that was it!* The universe had turned on me! I went to the toilet, slipped over in the mud and got scratched by a thorn. It was not my day.

On Saturday morning, it was freezing. Everyone woke up at six but had breakfast at eight and then got ready for the enormous hike...

Edith Beatrice Butler (10)

Laleham CE Primary School, Laleham

The Incredible Diary Of...

Dear Diary,

Today, as usual, I was lying in the same Lego tub, broken! I was waiting for my owner, Matt, to rebuild me back to my original form.

As I saw the beautiful daylight, I knew Matt had never forgotten me! As Matt rebuilt me, I noticed a new dinosaur Lego set that I could build, a T-rex, and everyone would think that Matt built it all by himself and no one would think that he was a bad builder anymore. So, when he went to have lunch, that is what I did. It took one hour to build but it was worth it to stop his family calling him a bad builder.

It worked! There was more to build, so why stop if there was more to build? So I built more! I built one after another, it was incredible. I was a master at building dinosaurs! I should do it more often.

Luca Stansbury (10)

Laleham CE Primary School, Laleham

The Incredible Diary Of...

Dear Diary,

Today, I have had the most fun I could have imagined. There I was, hanging on my favourite tree and then I saw a nice, tasty leaf. I went to get the leaf and then I heard it, the sound I never, ever wanted to hear - a sharp beaked eagle! *Run!* I thought. But it was too late, the eagle grabbed me. "This is the end for me!" I said in terror, looking at the horrible beast with wings.

Finally, the ride was over. The beast dropped me into her nest of five chicks and they looked hungry. I ran for my life and guess what? They caught me and they were trying to rip me to pieces. Then, I sang a lullaby and the birds went to sleep and I escaped!

Liam Blakley (9)

Laleham CE Primary School, Laleham

The Incredible Diary Of...

Dear Diary,

Today, I went to school. My grandad usually takes me, but he's in a different country, so now my family takes me in the car. I headed into the building and walked to my classroom. I put my bag and coat and hat in my locker and went to the classroom and sat and read a book. My teachers are called Miss John Lewis and Miss Lovell. They're the best teachers ever!

We started with maths first but sometimes the questions were a little bit hard for me. Break time was okay. When the whistle blew, we had to line up. Our teacher led us back to our classroom. Next, we had English, everybody found it a little challenging.

Then, we did Destination Reader, we were reading the BFG, it's a Roald Dahl book. We had to read some pages and do the questions. That was when it was lunchtime. I had chicken, cucumber, half a boiled egg, an apple and two bananas. I ate everything, but didn't finish the chicken. Lunchbreak was good.

I played with Pavel, then the whistle blew. We all headed back to the classroom. My teacher said to me, "Go to the library for a reading test." I became level thirty! When I got back, my class were doing art. They were drawing and then, Miss told us to get our stuff for home time.

Rylee Kyan Leach (9)
Preston Park Primary School, Wembley

The Incredible Diary Of...

Dear Diary,

This is all about my brilliant school trip and this is
how it began. We went on the train, but it took an
awfully long time to get off the train. After what
seemed like forever, we'd finally arrived.

As soon as we entered, I saw the London Eye. I was
more fascinated than ever! Then, we saw
enormous Big Ben and we went on a bridge, but I
was extremely terrified because I could see the
River Thames and I thought I would fall in!

We finally got to the boat. When we were on the
boat, there was a lady called Vicky who had a very
nice name and she was talking about all the places
in London. She was also very funny and honest.
Once we got off the boat, we ate our yummy
lunches because we were very hungry and my
stomach was rumbling.

After eating, we went to this place which was a bit
like a cinema. Instead of being 3D, it was 4D and
that was very weird to me, but maybe not weird to
other people in the room.

Once we exited the magical room, we waited for
the other classes. We decided to have a little bit of
food. At last, they came, so we left and went to the

train station. Once again, it took a long time and it was freezing cold outside!

Zeynab Shirzad (8)
Preston Park Primary School, Wembley

The Incredible Diary Of...

Dear Diary,

One time, I went with my family to Winter Wonderland. It was so big and beautiful, there were so many games and I tried some funny games. I was scared because one ride was tall. I asked the person there and he said, "You can go on because you're ten years old."

The rest of the rides were fun, the park was really brilliant and colourful!

The next day, I was sleeping and, suddenly, I woke up because I heard a sound. Someone was speaking. I thought it was just my dad who'd come home from work, but it was 10pm, my dad comes home at 11pm! My mum was sleeping in another room and my brother was at the gym. I was really scared! Suddenly, someone laughed. I said, "Oh my gosh. I can't even call the police!" I went into the room where my mum was sleeping and someone said, "Hello, how are you?"

I was confused, but I decided to go to the kitchen. It was just my dad speaking with his friend! He said, "Why are you so scared? Today I haven't been at work, don't you remember?" I started to laugh so much!

Mohammed Samir El Kordy (10)

Preston Park Primary School, Wembley

The Incredible Diary Of...

Dear Diary,

Two years ago, a three foot asteroid hit my backyard. I was full of awe. It felt like an alien had come from space and it was trying to take over the universe! Suddenly, the asteroid opened. A seven foot tall, 10,346 pound monster came out! I was shocked at its appearance. It was definitely not human, but it was harmless.

I thought if I helped it and gave it a place to stay, it would return the favour. I took him to the local park and told him about Earth. When he saw the basketball court, he ran and jumped with a basketball that was lying on the court. Without even looking, he did a slam dunk.

Two agents from the NBA saw him and called every team in the NBA. When I saw him, I was so shocked I couldn't move. The monster walked back and said his name was Dr Legend.

He asked, "Can we go back and play?" I was so happy, I said yes. More agents asked him to play for teams and he said yes. The team he picked is the best team ever: the Golden State Warriors. I haven't seen him since...

Ziad Lloyd (9)
Preston Park Primary School, Wembley

The Incredible Diary Of...

Dear Diary

One day, I went to school with THE best football player in the world, Messi!
When we played football in the playground, amazingly, I played like him. Everyone was intrigued and wanted to know how I was playing so well. I lied and said, "It's because of Messi's luxury cars!"
However, no one believed me because Messi is very famous and wouldn't have time to drop me, a normal boy off at school. I said, "How doesn't Messi have the time? He always finds the time to drop his sons off at school!"
Everyone was just jealous because I'd actually seen Messi, and as a result they tried to trick me into making me think that they'd seen Christiano Ronaldo too.
Everyone went silent, no one was talking, of course, they thought that I was eventually going to tell them all about my adventures with Messi and how I played like him, his habits and what his house looked like! But, that is Messi's little secret and mine. SSHHH!

Micah Levi Hibbert (9)

Preston Park Primary School, Wembley

The Incredible Diary Of...

Dear Diary,

I moved house last week. Before, I lived in a flat and I always got tired of going up and down the stairs. We started packing up and put all the stuff in the car. I got very excited and helped my dad with packing it up. It was very dark and cold.

We got in the car and started driving. There was no traffic at all! It was only a six minute drive. We got to the new house and we took everything out of the car. But, before we put the stuff in the house, I got a quiet look at it. There is a tree house in the garden and a lot of sheds.

I went back in the house and saw that the kitchen is very small and the dining room is next to the living room. There was only one sofa in the living room, but we'd get more anyway. There is only one bathroom on the second floor and there are three bedrooms on the second floor.

I got out of the house and started helping my mum and dad put all the stuff inside. I got really heavy stuff and took it upstairs and then, we'd finished!

Namo Wurmezyar (9)
Preston Park Primary School, Wembley

The Incredible Diary Of...

Dear Diary,

I woke up this morning and saw a tunnel in the garden. I changed my clothes and went outside. I jumped down the hole to see what was there then, at the bottom, there was a mystical world!

I saw a mermaid in the navy blue sea, the trees grew one centimetre per second, also growing emerald leaves. I couldn't believe it! One evil thing lurked down there, it was a black, super-sized, fire-breathing dragon with gnarling claws! It had a great wingspan of ten metres and was flying in its colossal cave of darkness. Then, its slim, yellow, intimidating eyes pointed straight towards me. It then shot its flaming fire towards me! I ducked and it hit a hideous beast.

Then, I realised it was trying to save me. I sat on its back and pointed at the hole. It flew up the ginormous hole with an ear-piercing roar. Once the news company had seen it, we were on TV! Then, I found out it had eternal life. It was an unforgettable experience!

Ismaeel Ali (9)

Preston Park Primary School, Wembley

The Incredible Diary Of...

Dear Diary,

One day, I smuggled a monster to school. Before heading to the car, I carefully placed the monster in my bag. He goes by the name of Globby. I felt quite brave and quite nervous about showing off Globby to my friends, but I was really positive about what was going to happen that day. I hurried to the car.

Soon after, we arrived at school. I could feel Globby moving around in my bag, I knew Globby was hot in there because I'd put a whopping pile of books in my bag. I felt bad for Globby, so I ran all the way to my class.

During the lesson, everyone was roaring, so I decided to show my partner, but it didn't go as planned. Suddenly, she shouted, "There's a monster!" Globby hopped onto the table and roared. Everyone ran out the door, but all I did was giggle and high-five Globby. I put him back in my bag. It was terrific!

Abigail Ayomikun Ogunlami (9)

Preston Park Primary School, Wembley

The Incredible Diary Of...

Dear Diary,

I heard my doorbell ring and, all of a sudden, I opened the door. I thought it was the postman because I'd ordered a red fidget spinner. Instead, it was an indignant monster that had glistening red cheeks and hideous, appalling, atrocious horns! He was an infant monster with mature claws. It was mind-boggling to look at his horns. It was a dreadful sight. He was nearly inaudible when I asked him why he was there. He cried, "I need a new home!" So I let him in. Then I invited him for a cup of tea until I saw his weird heart-shaped tail. I backed up in terror and I let him finish the tea I'd given him. I ran upstairs in fear and locked the door. The indignant monster came and he said, "Don't worry, I'm a friendly monster not one of the ones you see that scare you!" He came to me for a hug and then we became friends!

Andrei Ionut Antonie (9)
Preston Park Primary School, Wembley

The Incredible Diary Of...

Dear Diary,

Today, I went on an amazing trip. We went to London and it was my very first time on a boat! I was sitting at the bottom of this awesome boat and I saw a spectacular sight. *This is the best trip ever*, I thought.

Our tour guide told us all about the views we were seeing and I was excited to see all these famous landmarks. I saw an astonishing view of the Shard but the most wonderful sight was Tower Bridge. Seeing the London Eye from up close, I thought it was gigantic and so breathtaking. In addition, I also saw other landmarks, such as Big Ben.

I saw the 'Wobbly Bridge'. The tour guide told us, "It gets its name because, when the bridge first opened, it was only open for eight hours as it was very wobbly!" I would highly recommend this cruise to my friends and family, it was fantastic!

Amira Elmi (7)

Preston Park Primary School, Wembley

The Incredible Diary Of...

Dear Diary,

Yesterday, I went to the funfair with a unicorn. There was so much fun stuff to play on. My friend, the unicorn, jumped with joy. Her attitude grew more. I couldn't bear it. The only thing that calmed her down was candyfloss. She loved the taste and how it smelled in her mouth.

After our scrumptious candyfloss, we went to try some rides. The first ride was the merry-go-round. I chose the super speedy car and my friend, the unicorn, chose the Disney bus! We had so much fun!

When it was lunchtime, I had a vegetable salad and my friend, the unicorn, ate some fresh, tasty rice with red, juicy strawberries. When we were done, we went to try some other rides.

When it was the end of the day, me and the unicorn were so tired. We'd had so much fun!

lakshmi Sahasra Veluri (9)

Preston Park Primary School, Wembley

The Incredible Diary Of...

Dear Diary,

Today was the best day ever! It all started like this. It was early in the morning, 6am. Today, I was going to the awful funfair. Oh no! After all that, I got changed and ate breakfast. Then, we all set off. My little sister tried to cheer me up, but it was no use at all. It was a long and tiring journey. When we reached the funfair, I was shocked. It was full of outstanding rides! First, I decided to have a go on the Ferris wheel. I sat on a lovely comfy seat. We all started going up and up and up. Just then, I saw a unicorn! It was pink and fluffy and, best of all, she could speak!

Then, Mia the unicorn gave me treats. But, in a flash, I was back in my own bedroom. What was going on? What had just happened? It was so weird! Was I dreaming?

Anushri Saha (9)

Preston Park Primary School, Wembley

The Incredible Diary Of...

Dear Diary,

Today, I woke up in the morning. I was very tired, but I had to get up. I went into the bathroom, I took my brush and put toothpaste on it. I started brushing. Then, I went into my room and got changed into my clothes and I went swimming. When I came back, I had a shower.

After my shower, I went to Pavel's house for lunch. Before lunch, we played football, but we had to pass to a player and shoot the ball into the goal. After, it was lunch. I was in the dining room and I had bolognese and pasta for lunch. Then, after a little while, I went upstairs to play some computer games and some outside games.

Then, it was time to go and I went home. I really want to go to his house again. I really miss Pavel!

Param Bhatt (8)

Preston Park Primary School, Wembley

The Incredible Diary Of...

Dear Diary,

Today, my day started when I woke up at 6:50am. As normal, I got ready for school, had breakfast, got changed and brushed my teeth. When I arrived at school, I went to my class, Dev still had his own clothes on. I asked him what he was doing and he said he was going on a trip. I'd forgotten that Dev, Pranav, Shooq and Varagi were going on a trip.

I did maths and I only got one wrong! Then, it was break time, but I'd forgotten to bring a snack again. After that, we did English. We had to write a narrative in neat. For lunch, it was tandoori roast chicken.

After lunch, we drew Bruno Jenkins from The Witches. After school, I went to basketball club and scored from behind the hoop!

Rayan Salarzai (9)

Preston Park Primary School, Wembley

The Incredible Diary Of...

Dear Diary,

Today was a petrifying but peculiar day. It was the day we were going on a school trip. I'd been waiting for so long. While I was having my milk, I spilt it because I was too excited! I even got to school early, the gates still weren't open!

I stood at the door, already jittering with excitement. We'd left home at 8:15 and we'd arrived at 8:30. Luckily, me and my sister, Dhruri, sat together and we were going on the trip together. We held hands tightly because we were so excited. Then, the bus came. I was freaking out! I went on the bus, there was no one there. I checked in the driver's seat, there was no one there! I went outside and I was in Candyland...

Gabriela Orlinova Sirenyakova (9)

Preston Park Primary School, Wembley

The Incredible Diary Of...

Dear Diary,

Today was the craziest day ever! I was in my room when I heard a knock on the window. I opened the window to find out that it was Pikachu! He told me that he needed my help in Pokéland.

On the way to Pokéland, Pikachu told me the problem was a ferocious dragon that was destroying everything! Once we arrived, the dragon was making the place even nicer, not destroying it! But, it was destroying some things to make some more room. The dragon was just a new friend!

We made a home for the dragon and played for hours and hours until I had to go home. When I got home, Pikachu followed me and we played until bedtime. I can't wait to see what we'll do tomorrow!

Nicole Florentina Pasca (9)
Preston Park Primary School, Wembley

The Incredible Diary Of...

Dear Diary,

The other day, in a flash, I woke up from a near heart attack because of my nightmare. I'd been fighting Messi during a football match! For breakfast, I had a sausage with a fried egg, then I went to school.

In school, we went to boxing class. After school, we went to the funfair. I had tonnes of candyfloss, then we went on a roller coaster. After the funfair, we went to the zoo. We saw lions, zebras and monkeys. We fed them food and treats.

We then went swimming, to do taekwondo, karate, judo, wrestling, self-defence, kickboxing, football, basketball, hockey and cricket lessons! It was the best and most tiring day ever!

Tahar Bnouni (9)

Preston Park Primary School, Wembley

The Incredible Diary Of...

Dear Diary,

I went to the park with an odd person called Killingrand the monster! He was nine years old and his body was slimy and green.

As we went to the adventure park, we played football with the other two people called Sane and Salah. They were in our team. We played one-on-one and Salah won, but I was tired.

After they left, we went to the swings. Killingrand pushed me so high into the air, my body was shivering! Then, we had lunch. After, we went to play and Killingrand was the best at it. At least we had fun!

Vinithan Kamaleswaran (9)

Preston Park Primary School, Wembley

The Incredible Diary Of...

Dear Diary,

On Saturday, my family and I went to the park because my brother and I wanted to play football. After a long game of football, we decided to have a short break so we went Pokémon hunting. On the Pokémon map, I found Lugia and I wanted it because it was very rare.

Once I was done playing Pokémon, my brother and I were pretending to find treasure but, instead of pretending to find treasure, we actually found real treasure! There was a lot of gold and jewellery, so we took it.

Leart Thaci (9)

Preston Park Primary School, Wembley

The Incredible Diary Of...

Dear Diary,

Today, my friends came to my house and we made slime. We made fluffy and clear slime, it was so fun! The ingredients were: clear glue, a bowl, shaving cream, a spoon and activator. If we wanted, we could add any colour or design. I made fluffy slime and my friends made clear, pink and glitter slime. I added the pink. Then, we went to the park and played tag. Then, we went home and had dinner.

Diyana Kanbi (8)

Preston Park Primary School, Wembley

The Incredible Diary Of...

Dear Diary,

I've had the best day ever! I've finally been adopted! Now, I've got a room, some food, everything... and a mum! She has dark, long hair, lips as red as a red, red rose and eyes as brown as a bear.

We had such a fun day today. We went to the funfair, we watched a circus show, then we went shopping in Tesco. Then, we went to the Apple Store and got an iPad. I loved today!

Laksh Patel (9)

Preston Park Primary School, Wembley

The Incredible Diary Of...

Dear Diary,

One evening, I was in a mysterious forest with my family. In the distance, we saw an enormous shadow. Me and my family backed away, it was coming closer. I wished it was a dream but no, it was real!

After some minutes, I found an axe on the floor. I wanted to go and take it on and kill it, but my mum said no, so I didn't. But, a hero then came and saved us!

Lorena Maya Szabo (9)
Preston Park Primary School, Wembley

The Incredible Diary Of...

Dear Diary,

Today was the best day! Me and my brother, Leon, saw a huge dragon. It was mostly harmless, so we were allowed to pet it. But I don't even know what I was thinking... The dragon bit me, but not my brother! It was absolutely not fair. Thankfully, I'm okay.

Precious-Lyla Bridget Turgut (11)

Preston Park Primary School, Wembley

The Incredible Diary Of... Poor Mr Chair

Dear Diary,

Today was the worst day of my life! It all started on a rainy day. I was in the classroom, as peaceful as ever, until they came. I was just talking to Mrs Table, who was talking about how much she loved art and if she could, she would be a famous artist. Suddenly, they came running in, those monsters looking for the next thing to destroy. I watched as they came running in, one of those kids even sat on me! They started throwing things around the room like paint. They were mad!

All of a sudden, some kid came running in with paint in a bucket, throwing it everywhere. Luckily, not a drop fell on me, but most of it fell on Mrs Table. She was crying her heart out. She shouted, "I'm ugly! They've destroyed me! I'm hideous!"

I tried calming her down. I think a teacher came in and told everyone off. Then, suddenly, a really short kid stood on me. I was in pain. One of my legs broke off! The angry, depressed teacher picked me up and threw me out. I waved goodbye to Mrs Table and now here I am, behind the school in the rubbish bin...

Annabel Bernard (10)

Willow Tree Primary School, Northolt

The Incredible Diary Of... Mrs Kennedy's Pen

Dear Diary,

Today was the most magnificent day in the world. I was used twenty-seven times! My owner is a teacher, her name is Rachel Kennedy, but her students call her Mrs Kennedy. From what I'd heard, today was an independent writing day, so that meant children got POPs (paragraphs of perfection). Today was my time to shine!

I am kind of dumb in general as I'm a pen but, when Miss picks me up and writes with me, I somehow get super-duper smart! Anyway, as I was saying, today was independent writing day, so I was used a lot. When Mrs Kennedy picked me up to mark a few books, they had quite a lot of mistakes and barely any ticks, which made Mrs Kennedy feel so frustrated, she started to squeeze me. Can you believe it? I mean, I'm a pen, but I have a family and a life too!

When she got to the last book, she flicked the pages to the writing and started marking. Her frustration seemed to vanish. The first paragraph was full of ticks but, what caught my eye was that she was looking at the POP stickers. While she was reading the writing, she was giggling a lot, I could feel her blood cells laughing and moving around.

She then put me down, her hand slowly reached for the POP stickers and I couldn't believe my eyes. I started to sweat. It mean that I was running out of ink so Mrs Kennedy had to shake me. She got a POP sticker and gladly placed it on... I didn't know which book she was marking, but I was happy for them.

At the end of the day, I felt astonished as I felt special because I was used twenty-seven times!

Rosa Hosseini (11)
Willow Tree Primary School, Northolt

The Incredible Diary Of... Bethany

An extract

Dear Diary,

Today was so embarrassing! I want to cry and yell. I don't think I'll even get a wink of sleep tonight, I'll probably be thinking of how the day could have gone so much better. I hope tomorrow is way better.

As I woke up this morning, my sister approached me and held her phone against my face, sighing. School started at 8:25am and it was 8am. Worry filled my body; Jemma (my twin sister) threw my uniform at me. Without thinking twice, I put it on. Jemma grabbed my hand and pulled me through the door. The realisation dawned on me that we had missed the bus and we would have to walk. We were late. This wasn't the best start to a new high school. I walked into the classroom, head down, ashamed of being late. The teacher told me I was late, as if I didn't already know. Everyone began laughing at me and whispering. When I turned around, a boy was doing a rude gesture. I pushed his hand away as if I didn't care, but I did.

The bell blared, it was finally French, my favourite subject. "Bonjour, je m'appelle Mrs Franklin." The rest of French was fun, everything was good until PE. We had to do fifteen laps and, I must admit, I'm not the best at fitness as I have asthma. I began to feel more and more tired and, eventually, I felt as if I was losing all my breath...

Skye Nicholson (10)
Willow Tree Primary School, Northolt

Capture Your Life

Inspired by Minecraft Capture The Flag

Dear Diary,

It was life or death... I sprinted over the green grass and jumped into the wide pool of water. I put on iron armour, it was time to prepare. We couldn't cross the middle for four minutes, so it was a battle against the archers for now. I could see the wool sitting in the far distance, waiting to be taken. It was my time to shine.

It was thirty seconds until we could cross the middle as the 'half-bridge' was being 'corrupted' by war. I travelled to the enemy's base by water and stood on the bridge. A group from the red team stood in front of me. One hit with a sword and I would fall and go unconscious.

Filled with hope, I jumped on one's head and hit another with my sword. The wool was in my hands! All I had to do was go through a swarm of archers and put the wool into the projector. A hologram rose in the air and said we'd won one point!

I didn't want to let my team down, so I ran as fast as I could. At that moment, I went unconscious. When I woke up, I was badly wounded, but we'd won the match! I was thrilled. A young-looking boy explained that I was shot off a bridge with arrows and CatapillerMac took the wool from me and

captured the point for our team.
I still play capture the flag matches, they're fun but deadly...

Jemimah Esi Sackey (10)

Willow Tree Primary School, Northolt

The Incredible Diary Of... A Young YouTuber

Dear Diary,

It's only been about four days since I started played this creepy but surprisingly exciting game. Today was my best day ever playing this game and I've also earnt some good monetary results. You'll soon understand why this is not your usual everyday diary entry.

I wasn't in school today as we are on break for Easter. Today, after my early morning self clean, I went to my computer, ready to keep testing the new computer game. This game is due to come out in December 2019 (about eight months from now). There is not even a trailer yet for this game so this was special for me. I was also excited as this was my first time testing a game. I'd also been informed that reviewers may potentially be rewarded financially for their time.

Initially, when I began playing it, it felt really creepy, but as the game progressed, it became more exciting. I got to defeat all the little evil gremlins!

Later today, I checked my bank account. Guess how much I was paid for testing the game? I received a whopping £9,999,999,999!

Now I've got to stop writing so I can make another video!
Yours sincerely,
Alex.

Alex Wirekoh (10)

Willow Tree Primary School, Northolt

The Incredible Diary Of... Mr Crocodile

Dear Diary,

It was yet another day alone without my mother. I felt that life was now nothing more than a tragedy. Without her, life was not worth living, but I still had faith that she was still alive...

Just yesterday, somebody said that, apparently, my mother was still alive. Now my fellow comrades and I were on a search.

"We shan't be able to leave," I said.

"Why?" questioned Mr Alligator.

"Because humans will run away," I answered.

"Great," said Mr Alligator in a sarcastic tone.

All of a sudden, a letter came through the post! We opened it with our sharp teeth and read it.

'Dear son, I don't have much time to explain, but I am in the park.' It stopped there.

"Now we know where to look!" I said.

In the blink of an eye, we set off to the local park. The journey was tough, with all the humans screaming as we walked past.

Once we were there, I squinted to see my mother tied up with a rope getting set on fire by humans! I ran after then, but it was too late. She was dead...

Ilyas Omar (10)
Willow Tree Primary School, Northolt

The Incredible Diary Of... Rosa Parks

Dear Diary,

I am choosing to write today because it's an important day for me. I'm lucky I had a piece of paper and a pen with me so I can write down what I'm feeling right now. Today, I was arrested and I had never been arrested before. In fact, I'm in a prison cell at the moment. Why? Well, I'm not sure because I've not done anything to deserve being here. I'll tell you how I got here.

After work today, I was extremely exhausted and longed to get home. Thankfully, there was a seat on the bus, the last seat. My legs were aching and I breathed a sigh of relief as I sat down.

Shortly, a 'non-coloured' person boarded the bus, but all the seats were full. Almost immediately, the driver told me and some other African Americans to get up! "I'm sick of this inequality," I told myself. "I don't want to get up." So I didn't.

The bus driver threatened to call the police, but I didn't dare move. I had made up my mind. Soon, the police arrived. You can probably guess what happened next...

Melissa Andrea Mihaila (11)

Willow Tree Primary School, Northolt

The Incredible Diary Of... The Cup Final

Dear Diary,

Today was the worst day ever! I've just got back from the football game. It was the hardest game ever. We were at Wembley and were playing a football match. For the first twenty minutes, nothing happened. There were a lot of shots taken, but our keeper dealt with it and no one scored.

I wasn't playing; I was on the bench. In the thirty-third minute, they made an attack and scored. We were one goal down and everything went downhill. Just after half-time, I was put on. I was in midfield. I managed to get one shot and score, but it was offside.

In the seventy-eighth minute, I crossed the ball to my teammate. He scored. We didn't play attack, but it lasted for the rest of the match and it went into penalties. I was the first to take one and I scored! Just joking, I missed... It was terrible!

We ended up losing and I don't really want to talk about it. Tonight, I think I'll cry myself to sleep. Just so you know, the score was four penalties to them and two to us. I'm going to cry now.

Jay Hughes (11)

Willow Tree Primary School, Northolt

The Incredible Diary Of... The Suspicious Teacher!

Dear Diary,

This happened a couple of weeks ago and it still gives me the chills... When we first met our teacher, I was surprised and elated because she was the best teacher! But actually, she gave me a weird feeling. I'd never had that feeling ever before.

During class, I was wondering about this feeling. Was it fear? Was it anger? Was I surprised?

A few minutes later, I finally figured it out - it was my terrified reaction! I felt my heart sink in my stomach like I couldn't breathe...

After one hour, school was over. I decided to follow my teacher to see why I was terrified. When she started walking out of school, that's when my sneaky hiding skills began. It felt like I was a ninja from another century!

A couple of minutes later, we walked into a dead, dark hallway with skeletons and red blood on the floor! Seeing all of these things made me think that she was a murderer, a murderer who was wanted for three to four years. I still carried on following her to see if I was correct...

Tiffany Elena Nastasiu (11)

Willow Tree Primary School, Northolt

152

The Incredible Diary Of... My Lucky Holiday!

Dear Diary,

I've just come back home from the most amazing holiday! It all began when we (my family and I) went on a flight to Russia. After a long, tiring journey, we landed and made our way to our hotel, which was luxurious. The beds were enormous and comfortable. The ceiling was shining with diamond edges. It was so icy! Although we were there for two weeks, it didn't feel like a lot!

A couple of days later, my mum and dad surprised me with a ticket to the World Cup final! Words couldn't express my thoughts and feelings. It is certain that they were the best.

After we settled in, we got our food and drink for the day. I couldn't have asked for better! It was just then when the game kicked off. Unfortunately, there wasn't much to see until the second half came. There was an unstoppable six goals altogether - France four, Croatia two. It was after a short break that they got everything back on track, Kylian Mbappé and Luka Modri. It was a miracle!

Ali Shidane (11)

Willow Tree Primary School, Northolt

A Day In The Life Of A Glue Stick

Dear Diary,

I have just experienced the most breathtaking day in history! Today was a school trip and I was really excited because I thought I would stay at school, away from those nasty children who pick their noses, but no! I had to go because the teachers asked a child to get a glue stick for the trip because they would need one. Guess what? He picked me! I was chucked in a plastic wallet and we set off. Whilst we were on the coach, a child was bored, so he opened my cap and made a giant hole in my glue!

Finally, we arrived at the Natural History Museum. We were halfway through the museum and then this happened: the teacher trusted a four-year-old child to hold the plastic wallet! I couldn't believe it! What if I got lost? I would just be a lonely glue stick on the floor about to get stepped on...

This day was an unlucky day for me. We were walking and I slowly slipped out of the plastic wallet. I had to run after them so fast until I finally got noticed by a teacher.

Zara Delfi (10)

Willow Tree Primary School, Northolt

154

The Incredible Diary Of... How I Became The Flash

Dear Diary,

You won't believe what happened yesterday! I woke up and I went downstairs to have breakfast. There was a glass of juice on the table. I came towards it, it smelt like something I'd never smelt before. It was like... fire! There was an abnormal letter next to it. It read, 'Drink this now or you will die a painful death'. As I rapidly opened the lid of the juice, I carried on. I dropped to the floor. When I woke up, an ambulance was next to me. I asked them what had happened. They responded with bad news. "A beetle was in your mouth."

As soon as they'd finished telling me what happened, we were at the hospital. The doctors and nurses were trying to see what was going on with me. They figured out that I was like the Flash because I healed very quickly. Because of this, they let me go and I ran to my friend's house. When I got there, I felt zaps coming in and out of me. I was burning. I told my friend and he fainted!

Samuel Xavier Third (10)
Willow Tree Primary School, Northolt

The Incredible Diary Of... Me Winning €1,000,000 In The Fortnite World Cup

Dear Diary,
It all started when I was at home, playing Fortnite. I was at home when this new game mode came out called Arena. It was a type of tournament. I played and played, day and night, Arena mode was ranked.
I got to the champion rank and competed to get an invite to New York for the £1,000,000 tournament. You needed to have 500 points, I had 490. Scared but prepared, I thought I wasn't going to make it. Happily, I did. I was screaming in happiness!

Dear Diary,
I was in New York, competing. I was at the top of the league after five hours of playing someone called FaZe. Tfue was first with 1,023 points, I was second with 1,022 points. It was a one-on-one, me versus Tfue. I hit him with my shotgun, he was on ninety health points, I was on 200. I hit him again. As I panicked, I tried shotgunning him again.

I didn't look but then, everyone shouted my name. I'd won! I couldn't believe it. My life had changed.

Noris Ciobotea (10)
Willow Tree Primary School, Northolt

Incredible Adventures In The Rainforest

Dear Diary,

With the map I'd found previously on my journey, I discovered a temple in the Amazon rainforest! I found truly unbelievable treasures, but I also faced danger. Brilliant!

Firstly, I was walking through the rainforest when I saw a towering building - the temple. I was thrilled and my insides were racing with joy! I entered cautiously - I didn't want to get hurt.

Suddenly, I saw thorny plants as sharp as knives advancing on me. I was horrified! Luckily, I managed to escape in time and I saw the treasure...

Slowly, I marched towards the treasure. Little did I know that it would be a terrible idea. I grabbed the treasure and ran away, but the temple was collapsing! Why did I even take the treasure? I was trapped until a few people saved me!

I feel thrilled that, for the first time in my life, I went into a temple! Even though I was trapped, this won't stop me from continuing my adventures! Bye for now, Lina.

Anjali Kumar (11)

Willow Tree Primary School, Northolt

The Incredible Diary Of... Football

Dear Diary,

I'm a footballer called Cristiano Ronaldo and I am going to tell you what happened in the extraordinary match between Juventus and Tottenham. This was in Wembley Stadium.

After full-time, the referee pointed to the penalty spot as the score was nil-nil. The first person to take a shot was my best friend, Dybala. As the referee blew his whistle, he ran towards the ball and shot it into the back of the net. Then, it was the most magnificent player's turn - Harry Kane. As always, he scored. Then, my teammates, Cancelo, Kean and Bernardeschi, took a shot and, from Tottenham, it was Son Heung Min, Pelé, Alli, Rose and Lloris. Lloris missed.

I was the last person taking the shot. I was feeling nervous and apprehensive. If I didn't score, I couldn't take the shot again. The referee blew his whistle. I ran towards the ball like a cheetah and shot it... Goal! I had scored and my team had won!

Faizan Arshad (10)

Willow Tree Primary School, Northolt

The Incredible Diary Of... A Secret Unicorn In The Woods

Dear Diary,

You will never believe what I've just experienced. It sounds crazy, but it's true.

It all started when I was walking in the woods with my friend, Ariana. We were playing hide-and-seek, no one was there, just us. When it was my turn to count, Ariana started to hide, I knew she was a good hider. Once, we'd played hide-and-seek with Luka, Casey and Rineasha and it took Luka five minutes to find her!

I finished counting. I started to search, but there was just me. I didn't know where she was. The woods were deep, as deep as the sea.

Unexpectedly, my eyes caught onto a bush. The colour was a bit strange. It was green, pink, purple and white.

As I entered the bush with hesitation, I saw a unicorn! Did unicorns even live in the woods? Was it real? This was the best day ever for me. I wondered how Ariana was doing in her hiding place. This was the best day ever!

Abishna Bavan (10)

Willow Tree Primary School, Northolt

The Incredible Diary Of... Jackie The Potato

Dear Diary,

My name is Jackie, I am a potato. Who cares? On my birthday, I got a new jacket from my uncle, who got eaten, a pair of shoes from my daddy, who also died, and some shorts from my mummy, who passed away yesterday. Maybe it's a family tradition!

Dear Diary,

Jackie here again! I recently read a book called How To Make The Best Potatoes. It said that potatoes can be roasted, boiled, mashed and baked. Since it seems the best, I've chosen to be baked in the oven. I told Jeff, I'm so excited.

Dear Diary,

Today was my lucky day! Jeff was going to bake me for his dinner! I said goodbye to my siblings as I walked onto the tray and was pushed into the oven. There was an irritating sound above me and it was getting hot. I asked Jeff for a glass of water, but he didn't respond. Devastated, I opened the oven door, running away and laughing at him!

Kaizer Santillan (10)

Willow Tree Primary School, Northolt

The Incredible Diary Of... A Soldier Fighting In The War

Dear Diary,

I am a soldier fighting in the war for England. I am writing for what might be the last time because I know I will die soon. I feel nervous and scared at the same time. I feel like I'm about to explode.

A few hours ago, Germany attacked us and we lost over 500 soldiers! I just hope that I survive this hateful war. If I hadn't signed up in the first place, I would be at home, relaxing and watching TV. I was so crazy to join. Well, I just hope I live or I'll be dead in the middle of nowhere!

Oh no! I see German bomber planes heading towards us. They're shooting bullets at us...

Dear Diary,

I've been shot in the arm. There's no one around to help me. I think I'll die...

Wait a minute! I can see a British soldier coming towards me. He's going to put a bandage on me. I thought I was going to die, but I was wrong!

Saad Arshad (11)

Willow Tree Primary School, Northolt

The Incredible Diary Of... The Girl Who Turned Into A Fairy

Dear Diary,

I'm going to tell you how I became a fairy! It was a normal day when I woke up early to explore my father's lab. He'd always told me not to go in there but had never told me why.

It was 4am, an hour before my parents woke up. I silently crept into the lab. My mouth dropped. I couldn't believe it! My father was an inventor! As I passed all the inventions, I accidentally pushed a button, I was panicking. If my father found out, I would be dead! Nothing happened at first, but then I felt like I was shocked.

I woke up a few minutes later, everything was huge and my back felt funny. I got up and looked at the clock, which seemed really big. It was 5am. Oh no! If I was found there, I would be grounded forever! Then, I realised that I had wings. I was a fairy! I was really small, so I wouldn't be seen and that was how I became what I am now!

Prisha Anand Panchal (10)

Willow Tree Primary School, Northolt

The Incredible Diary Of...

Dear Diary,
Today, I did so well in my football league that I got scouted for a team. I've been scouted for Tottenham. I am so happy, even Neymar has been scouted!

Dear Diary,
Today, I was training and my friend, Neymar, got injured. He injured his foot because, when he tried to do a trick, he slipped. We have a match tomorrow!

Dear Diary,
We lost to Man City because we didn't have Neymar, but I haven't got upset because we have many more matches to go. Neymar is upset because he didn't get to play. My coach is furious with us, so we've decided that, in our next game, we will work harder. We have a game coming up and it is against the best team in the Premier League. This match is going to put us in first...

Dear Diary,
We won the match! This time, we've won the league and I am super happy!

Wisdom Djan (10)

Willow Tree Primary School, Northolt

The Incredible Diary Of... The Unexpected Worry

Dear Diary,

There is a lot of stuff I have to tell ya! Me and me poor wee'uns have been scootched out of our home. It was a madhouse filled with nutty people and the guy who ran it was bonkers I tell ya! Now, we're just old, nasty beggars roaming the street like nothing! There ain't nothing I can do about it! Oh golly gosh, I'm gonna go to the blooming workhouse if I ain't doing something. My poor kids! Oh boo hoo, I'm finished!

Dear Diary,

Thank the Lord, I'm saved! Me young'uns have some carers who gave them boots, so I guess they're okay. I'm gonna go to the workhouse after I say buh-bye to me kids. Oh, bless them all! May all happy things happen to clean, lovely kids!

Dear Diary,

Now I'm here, wound up in the blooming workhouse. I hope good things come my way...

Nelly Alina Siddiqi (10)

Willow Tree Primary School, Northolt

The Incredible Diary Of... The Exhausted Elevator!

Dear Diary,

Today, I worked so hard, according to me, going up and down. Oh, it's because I'm an elevator. Most of the time, I get exhausted, so I stop and then, I always get stuck.

There was this one time I got stuck with a man who looked like he was in a hurry and a woman who might've been going to an interview because she was dressed nicely. You never know. After an hour, which felt like a century, the man still didn't give up trying to open me and the woman just sat there, upset. I was even more upset that there were people standing in me!

They started to have a conversation, it started with the woman. She said, "There's no point, give up." The man didn't even reply, he carried on.

Moments later, there was a rescue crew out. They came to help and the man said, "Never give up!"

Ariba Ashiq (10)

Willow Tree Primary School, Northolt

The Incredible Diary Of... The Life Of A Mouse

Dear Diary,

I woke up in my warm bed and I went to eat my breakfast. I went to look in my fridge... I'd run out of cheese! I didn't want to face the hairy beast known as the cat.

As I opened my front door, I could see huge objects. Suddenly, I heard thudding and stomping. I went behind a tall, wooden object which I had left out and hid myself. When the thudding stopped, I scuttled up the fridge and opened it. I looked around, but I couldn't see anything! Were these people saying they hated cheese?

I heard a noise. Reluctantly, I turned my head to see the beast! When I ran, I stumbled across some cheese. It stank! I went back home, but the cat still chased me. I ran outside my house, I just had to try some of the cheese. Before I touched the cheese, the cat that was targeting me grabbed me and tried to eat me...

Mohammed Ayangar (9)

Willow Tree Primary School, Northolt

The Incredible Diary Of... The Mystery

Dear Diary,

Where do I begin? Today was the day me and my friends were visiting the haunted house on Horror Street. No one had ever been there, no one ever went anywhere near that house. Me and my friends agreed to meet at the haunted dwelling at 7pm sharp.

As I made my way down the road, a cold shadow rushed past me, but I didn't want to get scared already. When I arrived at the abandoned house, a wave of curiosity drove me closer to the door. I got a message from my friends telling me that they couldn't make it, so it was just me on my own. I twisted the door open and walked in.

The door slammed right behind me, I thought it was a bit strange. I carried on walking until I reached the stairs. A black shadow had appeared on the wall. I was so scared that I froze completely! A loud bang came from upstairs. I ran...

Sherry Ayazi (10)

Willow Tree Primary School, Northolt

The Incredible Diary Of... How I Became The Incredible Hulk

Dear Diary,

My name is Bruce Banner and I am a scientist currently studying lots of things. One fine morning, when I was walking to my lab, I heard a bang near the park, so I checked it out. Guess what? It was a green rock. I was starting to get a bit nervous and confused about what was happening. I took the green rock to my house and studied it for days. I didn't go to work for days because I was studying the rock. To me, it was amazing.

The rock had a lid, so I opened it. All of a sudden, it shot at me like a bullet and I fell to the ground, unconscious.

Hours later, I woke up, dizzy and with a headache. I heard police cars, so I followed them... I had become the Incredible Hulk! It must have been the green rock. Now I am the Incredible Hulk. I guess I'm stuck with this for the rest of my life...

Toby Stamford Frost Fountain (11)

Willow Tree Primary School, Northolt

The Incredible Diary Of... My Embarrassing Grandma

Dear Diary,

Today was the most embarrassing day ever! Even more embarrassing than me walking into a wedding with flip-flops on. It was just a normal school day yesterday until the teacher mentioned that tomorrow, our parents would come and see our learning. My parents were on holiday, so I was left with my grandparents. At least I had someone to go with (my grandma) but I already knew the day wouldn't go well.

Today, me and my grandma left the house and people were laughing on the way. We arrived at school and people were laughing about my grandma and gossiping. We went into class and everyone was staring at my grandma. It was awful. So, after class, my friends questioned me as if I'd just talked to the nerd. "What were you thinking?" they said. Well, that's all I have to say...

Nosia Ahmadi (11)

Willow Tree Primary School, Northolt

The Incredible Diary Of... Rabbit: A Plush Rabbit's Journey

Dear Diary,

Today, I faced the hardest decision: to leave or not to leave. All day I've been preoccupied by this life-changing choice. If I leave, Maisie will miss me. If I don't, I won't be able to live up to my full potential. I've seen this before... Maisie was watching a movie with her dad - I think it was a documentary - where a group of toys ran away. It seemed like a great idea at first, but then I thought of the consequences and I felt more reluctant.

Even so, I've decided I *will* run away! I know it sounds like a ridiculous idea, but I think I have an adventure on my hands. I've decided to set out tonight once Maisie goes to sleep...

I'm ready to set out with nothing except me. I've waved a fond farewell to my fellow toys and expect the worst...

Willow Gayle (10)

Willow Tree Primary School, Northolt

The Incredible Diary Of...
Goodbye Homework

Dear Diary,

Today, I had the weirdest time of my life and I wouldn't be writing this if I hadn't done what I did. I wouldn't have had time to!

It all started when my teacher gave me homework! I went home and did my 1,000 maths questions. Life is cruel sometimes. Anyway, I started thinking of how the smartest kid in school, George, was so good at this. Suddenly, I got a brilliant idea. I could use George's time machine and stop homework from being made!

I sneaked into his house, did my business and went back to school. I went over to a friend and they asked me, "Want to go to my swim party after school?"

I asked him, "But don't you have homework to do?"

He looked at me and said, "What's that?"

It worked!

Ryan Kennedy (11)
Willow Tree Primary School, Northolt

The Incredible Diary Of... When I Caught A Glimpse Of Torture

Dear Diary,

It was a wonderful sunny day as I was there, rooted to the ground with my other tree friends. Then the earth started rumbling. Groups of humans with sticks that had razor-sharp blades came. Their big cars had scissors!

One of the big cars hit my friend! Anger exploded from my roots!

Bang! An explosion deafened my ears. One of the bushes was set on fire. I couldn't just stand there, so I swayed my arms (branches). Hammers hit my stomach (bark). I moved in agony!

Then another group of humans came. I prayed to God for this to end, but then everything stopped. I opened my eyes and then all the attackers were handcuffed to the floor, but one was left standing. He had some kind of rocket launcher pointing at me! All I heard was *kaboom...*

Imran Thomas Ibrahim (9)

Willow Tree Primary School, Northolt

The Incredible Diary Of... The Pencil

Dear Diary,

Today was horrific because someone thought it was a good idea to take a metal thing and put it on me and twist it. It was cutting me! At least it didn't cut all of me.

Later in the day, someone found me on the floor since my last user rolled me onto the floor. That new someone then stole me! Now, they use me all the time! There's one problem though, they keep cutting me! I try to talk to them, to make them stop, but they don't listen...

Dear Diary,

She finally took me back to school. Now I could see my siblings again! One problem, she'd left me outside, alone in the rain! I tried to move under the roof, but I fell into a puddle. Great. I was all wet, how amazing. I was stuck there, getting wet and hoping that I'd get dry.

Anastazja Budzik (9)

Willow Tree Primary School, Northolt

The Incredible Diary Of...
Performing At Live Aid!

Dear Diary,

Hello darling! Today was one of the best days of my life! I performed at Live Aid! Well, we all did. Me, Roger, Deaky and Bri. We tried our best and did amazingly, although my throat was a bit rough. Oh, and Mary was there with her fiancé, Jim. It was perfect. I just wish that the cats were there.

The best part was that I didn't freak out. The sea of people overwhelmed me and my heart was pounding. Oh, you'd best believe me when I say I was scared! But words can't describe how amazing it was to see so many people supporting us. Every single one of them was a family member, a member of Queen. The journey has been amazing and I couldn't have done it without the boys. I'm glad to call them family. I love them all!

Willow Welsh (11)
Willow Tree Primary School, Northolt

The Life Of A Rabbit

Dear Diary,

Yesterday, the weirdest thing happened to me! It all started when I was brushing my teeth for a special day, which was my birthday. I went downstairs for some pancakes when, suddenly, my family started singing Happy Birthday to me. Then my mum gave me a charm with a button and she also gave me a rabbit.

After that, I went to my room and tapped the button that was on my charm. Suddenly, I turned into a rabbit and teleported to a place called Rabbit Life! There were loads of chocolate rivers and there were thousands of candy canes everywhere! Also, there were marshmallow trampolines and cakes scattered everywhere!

At midnight, I turned back into a normal human. Yesterday was the best day of my life! I hope you can keep this secret.

Sharon Thomas (10)

Willow Tree Primary School, Northolt

The Incredible Diary Of... A Footballer

Dear Diary,

I had been dreaming about being a footballer for years. I had been practising football each year and, every other birthday, I got a new football. I am now twenty-one. I wanted to play football for a team in the Premier League.

I played for Cardiff City, I played about fifteen games and my wage was £20,000. I told my manager that I wanted to leave, so I did. I went to Chelsea, I played 200 games and got £1,000,000. I left Chelsea and went to the best team - Barcelona.

I wanted to stay, so I did. I played a lot of games for Barcelona. My family came to my 299th game against Real Madrid. My manager sold me to a good team in France called Paris Saint-Germain. I played 400 matches with them and I got so much money!

Callum Ashley Burt (10)
Willow Tree Primary School, Northolt

The Incredible Diary Of... The Incredible First Goal

Dear Diary,

Man City got into the Champions League and I scored the first goal! Let me tell you what happened. First, what happened was that I got a text saying that Man City was in the top four and we could go to the Champions League. I was full of excitement.

The next day, we had our first game in the Champions League against Tottenham, held in the Etihad Stadium. I drove there in my car, trained and entered the stadium. It was kick-off. I passed it to Kevin De Bruyne, he ran with the ball and Eric Dier slide-tackled him and the referee shouted, "Penalty!"

De Bruyne sat there crying with his leg broken. As the referee blew the whistle to begin the penalty, I shot and hit the top right. That was how we won the game!

Jeshan Jega (9)

Willow Tree Primary School, Northolt

The Incredible Diary Of... My Devil Twin Taking Over My Life!

Dear Diary,

Today was the worst day ever because I summoned my devil twin at 3am and she tried to take over my life! How horrible is that?

While my devil twin was having fun with my life, I was locked up in her cage, probably never to be seen again. Could the day get any worse? To top it all off, I had no phone to call anyone and the room was flooding.

I had forgotten that I had a hair clip to pick locks. Thank you lock-picking lessons! Surprisingly, those lessons came in handy! I quickly unlocked the cage and the door and then sprinted to the gymnasium to send my devil twin back.

Once I got there, I reversed the words and sent her back to where she came from. That was close! She'd almost taken over my life!

Divya Krishnakumar (10)

Willow Tree Primary School, Northolt

The Incredible Diary Of... The Magical Forest

Dear Diary,

On a calm morning, I woke up in a hurry. It was moving day! All things were packed away, all we needed to do was pack all the boxes into the van, which would be pulling up pretty soon.

A couple of minutes later, I saw the van pulling up. I was very excited as it was my first time moving house. Soon, everything was in the van and off we went. The journey was very boring, but we were getting there.

In the end, we got there and I ran straight to the garden. I stood there. It was a forest! I went into it and, two minutes later, I saw something in the bushes. I hid behind a huge rock and peeked over it. There was a unicorn! Then, every day I went in there to find Crystal the unicorn, who I'd named!

Emily Maguire (11)

Willow Tree Primary School, Northolt

The Incredible Diary Of... The Rainbow Rangers

Dear Diary,

I was out with my friends (Rosie, Bonnie, Indigo and Floof) on a mission to save a turtle and some little fish that were trapped in a net. Rosie has strength power and a see-through tiara, Bonnie has a contractor mat and vision power and Indigo has speed power.

Rosie ripped the net and the animals were free! We got on the boat which belonged to a man named Prestin Cresten who only wanted money and to be rich. We went in, but he trapped us and shouted, "Booby trap!" He locked us in. With his giant robot claws, he picked us up and threw us in the sea! *Splash!* We were sinking! Even our powers couldn't get us out. We shouted, "Help..."

Hinda Ali (9)

Willow Tree Primary School, Northolt

The Incredible Diary Of... Flying To Mars

Dear Diary,

I had the craziest week! I went with my friend to Mars for a day and things went wrong. It all started when we went inside the rocket and, maybe about fifteen hours later, we reached Mars. I was so excited! I spent one day jumping all over the place.

When I got back in the rocket, I had a nap for three hours, but I woke up to the sound of my friend screaming that we'd lost an engine! I felt butterflies in my stomach.

After hours of screaming, we found out that we'd landed on the moon! Luckily, there were other people with a working rocket. Fortunately, they let us go to Earth with them.

Ever since then, I have never wanted to go back to Mars!

Rineasha Ghimire (10)

Willow Tree Primary School, Northolt

The Incredible Diary Of... My Life As A Tissue

Dear Diary,

Do you know how much I have to go through as a tissue? Anxiety overcame my confidence as it was blown away into nothingness. Once, I was living a happy life; I was in a package and we were all on top of each other like a tin of sardines. We laughed and laughed and enjoyed life when, suddenly, one of my friends was picked up by a sweaty hand. Before we knew it, he was covered in a green, sticky substance that stretched all over him. It was a horrible sight and, before I knew it, I was next... Sorry Diary, it's not my fault that I can't use water or soap because I'll break away. This is my last piece of writing as my future awaits me in the bin.

Kinga Dominika Tomasiak (11)

Willow Tree Primary School, Northolt

The Incredible Diary Of... The Magic Purple Crayon

Dear Diary,

I had been sent to nursery yesterday. It was huge and terrifying. Picking me up, the giants started rubbing me everywhere, on paper, card, the walls and other things. It hurt!

I started to turn a different colour. I started to turn grey! Everyone was shocked! I didn't know what to do. They threw me away and started to use my friends. I felt sorry for them, but I was hurt.

A few moments later, a little girl came up to me. She carefully took me in her warm, cuddly hands. She was taking me somewhere. She was taking me to her house!

When we arrived, she took care of me. I started to turn bright purple! I was elated. That was the best day ever!

Kavinela Tharmakulasingam (10)

Willow Tree Primary School, Northolt

The Incredible Diary Of... My Missing Pen

Dear Diary,

Yesterday, I noticed that something was missing. It was my lucky pen! I'll tell you how I lost it.

It all started when I was writing my homework at home. Mum told me to go downstairs for dinner, so I went down. I had spaghetti. When I went up to finish my homework, my pen was gone! I asked my mum if she had taken it because she wasn't there when I had dinner. It was a mystery to solve!

I checked everywhere, but I couldn't find it. It was late, like 9:30pm. I went to sleep.

This morning, my pen was on my desk, just as I'd left it before dinner. I was shocked, surprised and over the moon. I was full of different emotions!

Isha Dhipan (11)

Willow Tree Primary School, Northolt

The Incredible Diary Of...
Andres!

Dear Diary,

You can't guess what's just happened. So, it was the last game of the season and we were top of the league. We were going to face the second place team. We were only three points ahead of them, that meant that if we lost, we'd go down to second. But if we won, we'd win the league.

The game started. In the seventeenth minute, I scored, but it was offside. In the fortieth minute, I scored another goal, but it was offside as well. In the ninetieth minute, it was my last chance. It was a corner to the other team and one was coming to me. I got the ball and I scored the winning goal. We'd won the league!

Stephen Pavel Thomas (10)

Willow Tree Primary School, Northolt

The Incredible Diary Of... The Pain Of Being A Door Handle

Dear Diary,
Nobody could ever understand the pain of being a door handle. The heartaches I have to go through are unbearable. I wish people would just take more care when they throw their disgusting germs all over me. People don't realise that, when they approach, my insides scream, but my outsides show nothing. They make me suffer so much; all they intend to do it go to the bathroom, but no. I can feel myself smashing into a million pieces. Why can't people be more selfless and repair me, not stomp on me?

Dear Diary,
They've finally repaired me! I know it's going to happen again though, all of it...

Raisa Jaca (11)
Willow Tree Primary School, Northolt

The Incredible Diary Of... Me!

Dear Diary,

I was injured a few minutes ago by a human. They shoved me and threw me and it was just painful. I hurt my felt and my back, that's why I'm writing here today. Let me tell you all about it.

First, I was sleeping in my comfy pot then, suddenly, someone picked me up. My heart skipped a beat. Then, he scratched my back with a pencil. It was painful! Without breathing, he threw me back into the pot. I hurt my feet, it was horrible!

Plastic shattered down on my body. Everyone else was injured. Pencil was blunt, Whiteboard was messy, it was harmful. Why did they do it? Anyways, I'd better recover myself.

Dawand Rashid (10)

Willow Tree Primary School, Northolt

The Incredible Diary Of... The Blue Blu-Tack

Dear Diary,

Oh! How? My baby has died. She didn't even last a week! She was so soft... Oh, dear Bluey, what will I do without you?

Let me tell you the story: she was Blu-Tack. Her name was Bluey. One day, I looked under the school table, waiting, looking for dear Bluey.

But oh no! She wasn't there! It wasn't fair. It wasn't my fault! It was them! They squished and squeezed her! They flattened her and threw her!

The teachers stuffed me under the desk. Oh, how I cried and cried, but no one understood me. I will get another one, but it won't be the same.

I will never forget you, Bluey.

Thisana Manoharan (11)

Willow Tree Primary School, Northolt

The Incredible Diary Of... The Special Pencil

Dear Diary,

Where do I begin? I was just so grateful to have this special pencil. There's a whole list of things that it helped me with, but the main thing was drawing. I drew every day with my pencil! However, one day, something traumatic happened. The pencil's lead broke! My eyes filled up with tears and I felt like screaming. I sharpened it perfectly. That pencil was so unique, but after that scary event, it turned into an ordinary pencil. I used to smile every day, but that changed at the speed of light! I keep my collection of pencils in my drawer, but that one was special to me...

Sasha Morris (11)

Willow Tree Primary School, Northolt

The Incredible Diary Of... PC Issues And Errors

Dear Diary,

I need to really tell you this because whoever bought me and used me didn't charge me when they left the room. This kid always played games on me and I was his toy. He always raged when I got a lot of errors. He would waste money by destroying stuff from his rages. I feel like this kid will get a new computer instead of a PC because he's put me in the basement because I have error issues. I always feel strange and weird down here. They haven't used me now for two months. They won't use me again, the issues were too annoying for everyone...

Nojus Arminas (10)

Willow Tree Primary School, Northolt

The Incredible Diary Of... The Singing Dragon

Dear Diary,

Today was amazing! This morning, I was in the jungle looking for food. Suddenly, I heard a rustle behind a bush. I thought it was a hunter, but it was a nice lady who was lost. She was surprised to see me (I'm a dragon). She asked me if I could breathe fire, but I can't. Instead, I sang a common English song. She was amazed! She grabbed me and took me to a famous person in England. I sang again and won over £100,000! Amazing, right? Overnight, I was known to everyone!

I have to go sing to the judge now. Bye!

Lilly the dragon.

Chenara Guruge (11)
Willow Tree Primary School, Northolt

The Incredible Diary Of... Dean Ambrose

Dear Diary,

Today, I have won a match and also Wrestlemania! I trained for days, months, years even, until this match. Let me express my feelings...

Before the heart-breaking match, I was interviewed by Shane McMahon. He asked what I thought about my opponent, Seth Rollins, my old teammate. I felt quite confident!

During his theme song, he was flexing on the crowd. After, I emerged from the crowd... Then it happened, the game started.

I got on the top rope. I jumped off and got RKO'd, but I still reversed and got him. Now I am the champion!

Steven Duffield (11)

Willow Tree Primary School, Northolt

The Incredible Diary Of...

Dear Diary,

One day, we were at school at Willow Tree Primary. We were writing a diary. Miss was looking for a whiteboard pen to demonstrate. The teacher's greedy hand reached out towards the pen pot! Second by second, her greedy hand reached closer and closer towards it. Then she started writing. "Argh!" screeched the whiteboard pen. "That hurts!"

It stopped working. It dried out completely!

Well, that was a weird day at school. Anyway, I have to go now, I have to do my homework. See you next time!

Natalia Mioduszewska (11)

Willow Tree Primary School, Northolt

The Incredible Diary Of... Unicorn And Me!

Dear Diary,

Today has been the weirdest day ever! To start it off, I was just walking across a field and I came upon a unicorn. She looked cold and unhappy. Suddenly, she spoke! I was so shocked. She said she was lost and couldn't find her family, so I decided to help.

I asked where she last saw them. She said that she had seen them in the forest, so I took her there. They weren't there so we kept looking. Moments later, we found her parents! They were so relieved and thanked me for helping. That was my crazy day!

Alicia Cook (10)

Willow Tree Primary School, Northolt

The Incredible Diary Of... An Astronaut On The Earth

Dear Diary,

It all began at night when I dreamt about going up in space. I was dreaming about a space shuttle with me inside saying, "To space!"

When I finally decided to look out the window, my eyes were about to burn as if I had directly looked at the sun! This was my first time in space and I really enjoyed it.

Then it was the boring part, going back home. I got back inside the space shuttle and went down until I could see my house again. I went back to bed.

Nomaan Khawaja (10)

Willow Tree Primary School, Northolt

The Incredible Diary Of... RoadTrip Jumping Out Of My T-Shirt

Dear Diary,

Today was an outstanding day. Who could ever believe this? I met RoadTrip in the strangest way. I'm still freaking out!

It was non-uniform day, so I decided to wear my RoadTrip t-shirt. I put my things away in the cloakroom and, soon, I felt something on my shirt. I looked at it and was pushed to the ground. Mikey was in front of me! I slowly blinked. Finally, all five of them were in front of me! It was the best day of my life.

Caoimhe Gannon (10)

Willow Tree Primary School, Northolt

YoungWriters
Est. 1991

The Incredible Diary Of... Billy Hope's Amazing Knockout

Dear Diary,

You won't believe what happened yesterday. I knocked out Escobar out of revenge for my wife, who died at a party because someone shot her! My daughter cried that day, I shouldn't have told her. I wish I hadn't punched someone in the face. It was the worst day of my life.

It was a good thing that I knocked someone out, but the bad thing was that my wife died. I always knew I had to get revenge on Escobar at least.

Joshua Ronald Albert Ryan (10)

Willow Tree Primary School, Northolt

The Incredible Diary Of...

Dear Diary,

Today, Poplar Three came to the library and don't get me started on what happened. The children love Beast Quest and I'm one of the Beast Quest books. People like ordering Beast Quest, but that isn't the worst part. Whenever I am taken out, I'm not treated the way I should be! I just get thrown into their school bags and get all bent and they don't even read me sometimes!

Iman Yassaa (10)

Willow Tree Primary School, Northolt

YoungWriters®
Est. 1991

Young Writers Information

We hope you have enjoyed reading this book – and that you will continue to in the coming years.

If you're a young writer who enjoys reading and creative writing, or the parent of an enthusiastic poet or story writer, do visit our website **www.youngwriters.co.uk**. Here you will find free competitions, workshops and games, as well as recommended reads, a poetry glossary and our blog. There's lots to keep budding writers motivated to write!

If you would like to order further copies of this book, or any of our other titles, then please give us a call or order via your online account.

Young Writers
Remus House
Coltsfoot Drive
Peterborough
PE2 9BF
(01733) 890066
info@youngwriters.co.uk

Join in the conversation!
Tips, news, giveaways and much more!

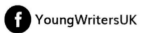 YoungWritersUK    @YoungWritersCW